Nine young friends find themselves in

invited by ace storyteller, Areen, to pa

made out of his fine gift of storytell

stories personally, and are moved to s

In the process, they are reminded of

have encountered in their own lives and are often also found voicing their disagreement with certain aspects of Areen's stories. Encouraged by him at the end of his stories, they undertake an insightful exploration of their identity, purpose in life, relationships, the values they need to uphold, and everything that makes life more meaningful.

Sangeeta S. Bhagwat likes to describe herself as an Inner Landscape Artist. Focusing on inner work to bring about outer change, she facilitates healing and transformation in individuals and groups. She has alternated between being an author and a Life Coach, since 1991.

Overcoming various personal challenges from an early age has helped Sangeeta build the compassion, understanding and strength required for inner work. She specialises in helping community and thought leaders in actualising their fullest potentials.

Since 2004, she has facilitated workshops to empower people to deal with their individual, emotional and physical problems.

Sangeeta has authored several articles, blogs and four other books on healing and self-empowerment. Her first book was translated into Marathi and her book on Emotional Freedom Techniques has been translated and published in Latvian.

For more information: www.serenereflection.com

Looking Back Looking Beyond

SANGEETA S. BHAGWAT

First published in 2013 by

OM

Om Books International

Corporate & Editorial Office
A-12, Sector 64, Noida 201 301
Uttar Pradesh, India
Phone: +91 120 477 4100
Email: editorial@ombooks.com
Website: www.ombooksinternational.com

Sales Office
4379/4B, Prakash House, Ansari Road
Darya Ganj, New Delhi 110 002, India
Phone: +91 11 2326 3363, 2326 5303
Fax: +91 11 2327 8091
Email: sales@ombooks.com
Website: www.ombooks.com

ISBN - 93-8260-740-4

10 9 8 7 6 5 4 3 2 1

Printed in India

For the Storyteller in each of us

"Develop an interest in life as you see it; the people, things, literature, music—the world is so rich, simply throbbing with rich treasures, beautiful souls and interesting people. Forget yourself."

—Henry Miller

"When you are joyous, look deep into your heart
and you shall find it is only that which has given you sorrow
that is giving you joy.

When you are sorrowful look again in your heart,
and you shall see that in truth you are weeping for
that which has been your delight."

—*The Prophet*, Kahlil Gibran

"Allow your judgments their own silent, undisturbed development, which, like all progress, must come from deep within and cannot be forced or hastened."

—Rilke

Introduction

A single candle lit up the porch. The night was warm, but there was a breeze just cool enough to keep the lazy youngsters awake. In the distance, Shantivan hill stood firmly against the sky.

"What now?" sighed Arya the youngest and most impatient of the lot. "No electricity means no computer, no internet, no play-station, no television! What did people ever do before all this got invented?" he wondered aloud, as he rapidly texted a few SMSs. Much to his dismay, he realized that his mobile's battery was running dangerously low.

"What could they do? They slept early!" was Ayushi's sarcastic rejoinder. "Early to bed and early to rise, that's what we are learning here, right? A return to simple living."

"Oh please! How boring today was," interjected Swapnil. "The trek up that huge mountain and that long lecture on how the local community there has developed self-sufficiency seemed like it would never end."

"Exactly," said Soumya, joining in. "And the icing on the cake was the bit about water conservation and how it has helped them in their crop cycles. If more of this is to follow in the days to come, we are doomed."

"You know!" Arya cried out in frustration, "When my parents signed me up for this, I clearly told them I would need my gadget time at night. Little did I know that electricity itself would be in such short supply here. Just imagine, power cuts at 8 p.m.! We have never had to deal with such things back home." Pausing for a moment, he frowned. "I wonder if my parents were already aware of this? Hmm..."

The others burst into quick laughter, leaving little doubt as to what they thought of the matter.

At this point, their host for the evening quietly walked in, holding a lamp in one hand. A rather thin, tall, middle-aged man, he set his lamp down next to the dwindling candle and greeted everyone with a warm, "Namaste."

Acting according to what had been drilled into them since childhood, the boys and girls mechanically stood up and greeted him with folded hands. At this, the man smiled to himself and gestured to them that this was unnecessary and they should remain seated.

"So, are you all comfortable?" the man asked gently, as he looked around in amusement at the unruly manner in which they were sprawled all over the porch. He made sure that he made eye contact with each of them individually. It was clear from the way he did this that he recognized who they were.

The first thing that struck the youngsters about their host was the sincere smile on his face. It did not seem just for the sake of formality, nor did it seem exaggerated, as if he were trying too hard to appear happy. He seemed genuinely glad to be where he was, to do what he was doing; glad to have the opportunity to interact with the people before him, strangers though they may be. His graying hair, gathered at the back of his neck into a short pony-tail, and his finely trimmed beard and moustache gave him a modern, worldly look that seemed in contrast with his simple clothing and the rustic surroundings he inhabited. A tinge of sadness in his eyes indicated that he had had his share of difficulties in life, yet the look of calm on his face and the equanimity in his demeanour, seemed to suggest to most people that he knew something they did not know, but should. The nine boys and girls before him were no exception, and even though they were themselves not fully aware of it, they were absorbing all of this.

"Ok friends, I have gone through the forms all of you were asked to fill out this morning and hence know a little about each one of you. But not all of you know me, so first a little about myself and what to expect here. My name is Areen and I would like to be addressed as just that, without any suffix or prefix. As you may have guessed, I will be acting as your guide during your stay here.

"Before we begin, I would like to clarify a few things. I am very much an ordinary person, like the rest of you. I will not be teaching you how to harness the 'powers of the subconscious mind' or how to bring about 'the instant manifestation of all that you desire.' I do not have any special formulae, keys or laws to give you which will unlock the 'secret' of life, or guarantee you 'success' and make you 'instant millionaires.'

"After our interaction is over, everything will not automatically fall into place for you, and you will still have to continuously evaluate your own choices, to apply your mind afresh to the different situations you encounter in life and it will still be up to you to work towards and hold on to what you care for, or let it slip away. It will be in your hands to let life go on as it did before, or respond to it differently.

"And yet, despite what I have just said, I do believe that I have 'something' of value to share with you; something I have learnt both from books and from experience, which may help you in navigating your own life. Similarly, I also welcome you to share your own experience and insights. I believe there is much to be learnt from each other, as no two lives, experiences and perspectives are completely the same. The more we listen to one another, the more enriched we are. I would like to create a space here that encourages you to speak freely. There are no 'right' or 'wrong' answers that I am hoping to elicit out of you. If, at any point, you cannot understand something, or even disagree with something I have said, please do not hesitate to ask or contradict me. All I request is that we speak respectfully and allow each one here to be heard."

After Areen finished his introduction, there was complete silence. The speaker's forthright manner had struck a chord with the group, but they were not going to admit it so easily, neither to themselves, nor to each other.

Deciding to put Areen's words to test, Malhar raised his hand and candidly confessed, "Very well, Areen, to be honest, we are rather bored here! Is there anything you can suggest to counter that?"

"Yes," Arya joined in wryly. "We are not used to such calm and quiet!"

Areen's smile grew broader and, rubbing his palms together for some warmth, he said, "Yes, I understand. So let us make things interesting. May I invite you to join me for a game?"

The mere mention of that last word immediately stirred the group and Areen was faced with an onslaught of excited questions.

"Finally, something fun to do! Where do we have to go? I'll go put my shoes on."

"What kind of game is it?"

"Is there some video game parlor around here?"

Areen gestured to his students to quieten down and answered, "No, I am afraid this might be unlike most games you are used to. But let me assure you, it is something very interesting. You'll have fun, don't worry." Nonetheless, it was quite evident from the puzzled looks on their faces that they were rather skeptical of what this simple-minded villager could offer city veterans like themselves that they had not already seen.

"Ok, show us what you've got!" challenged Arya.

"Well, actually, this is something as old as the hills," said Areen, noticing all the eager anticipation on the boys' faces immediately turn to disappointment the moment they heard the word 'old.' He continued unfazed. "I will be the raconteur for the night."

"Huh? What's that? What hardware does this game need?" asked Arya.

Areen chuckled good-naturedly. "This game uses one of the most advanced softwares ever developed." He pointed to his head, "Your imagination. That is all that we need. You could say that your brain is the hardware and your mind is the software. These are the only system requirements." The bemused friends could do nothing but look at each other, hoping for some clarity. "Yes, we tend to forget how much these two can do by themselves," Areen continued.

"So what's a raconteur?" asked a baffled Aditi.

"A raconteur is a person gifted with the fine art of storytelling. Right Areen?" replied Sheetal.

Areen nodded in response. "You flatter me Sheetal. But yes, essentially, it will be my attempt to hold your attention with some simple, light-hearted stories. There is something more to this game, though. After narrating my story to all of you, I will give you as much time as you would like, to reflect upon it. The floor will then be open for discussion. I encourage each of you to engage with the ideas in the story, supporting them, modifying them or challenging them as you see fit. If the story relates in any way to certain personal experiences of yours, which you would like to share, you are more than welcome to do so. Pay keen attention to what touches you deeply and what strikes you as discordant; and as long as you are being true to yourself, do not be afraid to voice your opinions. Do not relinquish your beliefs easily, but also be willing to admit when you are wrong. Be open to learning from others. Each of us need not agree on everything nor feel compelled to arrive at a consensus on every issue. As long as you are convinced of it, each of you can have a different perspective and there is nothing wrong with that. Once a particular conversation is complete, we can then move on to the next story." Pausing for a moment, Areen then emphasized, "Play the game in the right spirit and you'll see that learning and fun are not as far away from each other as we usually think them to be."

Areen looked on calmly as the boys exchanged dubious glances among themselves. Nobody had really said such things to them before and they did not know how to react.

"You know, rumour has it that this man is extremely eccentric. He sleeps for only about five hours a day, and has deliberately chosen to wear just three pairs of clothes for his entire life," muttered Drishti to the others.

Aditi whispered, "I overheard my parents mention how he was once fiercely ambitious and believed he was born to be a great man. However, a personal tragedy affected him tremendously, humbling him and making him more empathetic towards others."

"Oh, I don't know care who he is, or was. I don't think I can take those clichéd, moralistic lectures anymore. The ones I get at home are enough!" replied Arya under his breath.

Soumya's hushed suggestion was, "Look guys, we have nothing better to do in any case. We have been around him for some time now and you have to admit, there is something appealing about the man. I didn't really understand all that he said, but it did seem kind of interesting. What have we got to lose in listening to him? Let's give him a chance."

After a round of nods in agreement then, all of them went on to rearrange themselves into a circle around the lamp.

Sensing that it was time to start, Areen walked over to a cupboard in the corner and returned with a beautifully decorated wooden box.

"What is that?" asked a curious Arya.

"Well, each of the stories I am going to tell you, I remember with a special fondness, because I cherish dearly what they brought to my life. As a reminder of what each of them means to me, I keep a small token in this box, my 'Box of Tales,' as I have affectionately named it. I would like to share some of these tokens with each of you at the end of our short sessions. That way, you can each carry home a tangible souvenir of our time together."

His audience was intrigued and ready to listen, Areen went on to open his Box and carefully drew out a bright, shimmering crystal. Holding it before the flickering light of the candle, he began his first tale.

1

In the world of Becaamer, a group of teenagers would gather at dusk, underneath a tree, and discuss the happenings of the long and tiresome day gone by—what some of them did wrong, what went right for some others, how they could help each other improve, what faults they found in each other, and so on. Amidst these animated conversations and long silences, they strengthened their bond of friendship. Sometimes they would collectively break out into jovial laughter, at others they would argue fiercely and even depart bitterly; however, whatever the situation of the previous day may have been, the next evening they could be seen back again under the tree, valuing the relationship they shared above all differences.

Thanks to the efforts of the local teacher, who taught at the makeshift school under the oldest peepal tree, each child was encouraged to believe that he could be a gift to the world. Hari Master would patiently spend hours with each of the twenty-one children under his care. Strict when necessary, but more of a friend than a teacher, he would inspire his students to think for themselves. Not in favour of providing readymade solutions to their questions, he urged them to find their own answers, instead.

The parents of these children, however, were not very pleased with their growing ambitions. "Why are you making dreamers out of them?" they would ask him. "Don't you know that we can't afford to send them to the city for a formal education? There is no exciting escape waiting for these children. We send them to you to learn to read and write. That's enough for them to do better than us. Don't teach them to ask for more. It will only lead to disappointment."

Hari Master could understand their concerns, but he also had faith in his own teachings. "It is not like that. Do not mistake their confidence for arrogance or vanity. There is much more to life than what textbooks or rote-learning can teach us. To the extent that I could, all I have done is tried to make these children think independently, make them aware of how each one of them is unique, and taught them to celebrate that uniqueness rather than shy away from it. This will surely help them live fuller, more satisfying lives. I'm convinced about that, trust me."

The parents scoffed at him, but were helpless in the face of their children's enthusiasm. Rati promptly reminded her mother, "You no longer have to believe the nonsense the *zamindar* tells us about how our debts keep multiplying without our knowledge, I am intelligent enough to point out where he is manipulating us. And what would Jassi Masi have done without the help of me and my friends? Remember when the rains brought her roof down? It was all of us who helped her rebuild it using the few logs lying nearby."

Sunder was equally proud of his abilities. When his father questioned the usefulness of his evening discussions, he confidently replied, "Father, you know very well what went on in your shop before I joined. Have some of my ideas not increased our sales? It is my open and honest discussions with these friends and with Hari Master that have allowed me to think in innovative ways."

Somewhere, deep in their hearts, all the parents did think well of the work their children were doing. Their contributions to the community, such as the robust raft they had recently devised to carry more load than existing ones, were significant improvements. More goods could now be ferried across the river in lesser time, and the villagers got a better price for their wares in the city. However, there was this other side; parents which could not understand why the children would not willingly accept everything that they said. While the parents had faithfully obeyed their elders, these children would take very little at face value and tended to question them a lot. They would then make choices based on what they felt was right, rather than simply giving in to their parents without a fuss. This issue became most contentious in matters of career decisions.

For instance, Hafiz's father had been trying to reason with his son for the longest time, using the oldest argument in the book: "We never did this. Why must you?"

Hafiz would look back, wordless but defiant.

"We grew up and did what our fathers and forefathers have done for centuries. That is life. I am proud to continue the family tradition of gathering medicinal herbs. Why do you feel you should be different?"

"But, I do feel I am different father," Hafiz would respond finally. "All of us are. Each one of us is capable of unique achievements. Wouldn't you want me to shine in whatever I think I would be best at, rather than force myself to do something I am not really interested in?"

"Of course, my son. That is why I am encouraging you to take up the family profession. I'm sure you will really excel at it. I will gladly teach you the best methods of identifying the most valuable plants myself. All the wisdom our past generations have left behind will make you the best medicine harvester there is. You will see..."

"You may be right father. Perhaps that's why I was born your son..." His father heaved a sigh of relief, only to be cut short. "But then again, perhaps that is not true. Maybe I was born as your son so that I learn about these plants, but do something very different with that knowledge."

Hari Master, who had been listening patiently to the conversation, interjected, "Yes! Perhaps something different, *despite* that knowledge."

As soon as he heard this, the face of Hafiz's father's was flushed in anger. "Hari! What do you mean by that? Are you trying to say that only what you teach is useful and what we have learned through decades of blood, sweat and tears is worthless? How dare you try and turn my son against me!"

Hari Master continued speaking calmly, "Do listen to me. I respect your family tradition. But if we only blindly followed what was handed down to us, without exercising our minds at all in trying to improve things further, would any change in the world have been possible? Of course, we all have our roots, and I do not think there can be anything absolutely original, in the sense that it is completely unrelated to anything of the past. That, indeed, is how we are indebted to tradition, and that is why we should respect it. But why should that prevent us from looking to see if we can come up with something better? Unquestioned assumptions can keep us trapped in practices that have long outlived their original relevance or purpose, is it not?"

Hafiz's father was silent. He could see wisdom in Hari Master's words. But he had lived life as an obedient, unquestioning son. His own limitations prevented him from understanding all this at once. Ending his own internal debate, he shrugged helplessly and walked off.

Hafiz, too, was clearly upset by the conversation. He was familiar with this situation, and also familiar with his own response to it. It was easy to be an independent thinker when the stakes were not too high and the consequences short-term. But this was no small matter. It was a question of Hafiz's career. "Father is always making me feel guilty about who I am! Doesn't he realize that my dreams are also important? If I do what I love for a living, I will automatically make the effort to do it well, and not only my family, but other people too may benefit from it! But when Father goes on like this, I have serious doubts about myself. Is each person really specially talented? Wouldn't it just be easier to follow the family trade? Most people do so and they have been doing so for donkey's years... Who am I to be different then? Perhaps it's just me who is the stubborn mule and refuses to conform... How do I decide what I want to do... I'm so unsure of what I want..." he ended ruefully, looking at Hari Master for some consolation.

His teacher, however, was not as accommodating as Hafiz had expected. "Hafiz, we have had this conversation several times before. Do not doubt yourself so much. You have shown me several of your paintings, and I have told you without the slightest bit of exaggeration or sugar-coating, that you have the talent to be a good painter. That you love painting is clear from your work. Why then do you continue to paint only sporadically, just showing your work to me and a few friends? Why not go ahead and do it for a living? If you are worried you will not earn enough, well then that is a choice you will have to make. It is unfortunate that we live in a society that does not recognize the importance of art as much as it should, but that is how the situation is and it is not going to change immediately. But do you want to live your entire life regretting a lack of courage in expressing your natural talent? You have to take a decision at some point or the other. Think about it for yourself, introspect, and decide which way you want to go."

Hafiz tried to interrupt with some questions, "But how do I..." but was cut short sternly by Hari Master.

"The world does not owe you a favour, Hafiz. If you don't even begin to help yourself, why should you think help will be forthcoming from other quarters? You know the answer, Hafiz, you just have to confront it. Your challenge is not about discovering your calling. It lies in finding the courage to acknowledge it." Having finished what he had to say, Hari Master went away, leaving Hafiz deep in thought.

Rather than offering the usual words of encouragement, Hari Master had been frank and firm with him. This was not what Hafiz had really wanted to hear. Disappointed by this unexpectedly harsh treatment from his mentor, Hafiz went straight to his room. Deeply upset, he sat with his hands covering his face, his eyes shut, and a series of thoughts racing through his head. Nonetheless, somewhere in his mind, he too knew that enough was enough and he had to come to some kind of a conclusion now. He thought long and hard, and ultimately, finding no better way to vent, began to paint. He sat up till three o'clock that night, focused single-mindedly on his work, determined to let out all that was in his heart. Finally, satisfied with what he had created and feeling emotionally quite relieved, he gave the painting its finishing touches and held up the paper before his eyes, proud of what he had made—a young man with a mixture of both fear and hope on his face, desperately holding on to a rock, in the midst of a river, whose current is working against him, with the shore not far away.

The moment he woke up in the morning, Hafiz hurriedly put on his slippers, freshened up and, without caring for breakfast, ran to the peepal tree under which Hari Master could perpetually be found. He was reading a book at the time and was a little taken aback when he suddenly saw Hafiz standing right before him, short of breath, with a painting in his hand. Hari Master looked at the boy's work, and within a few seconds, a warm smile appeared on his face. His eyes misted over. "This is really well made, Hafiz. I told you, you are very talented."

Delighted at his teacher's approval, the young boy unselfconsciously blurted out all that was going on in his mind, "Hari Master, I do not have it all sorted out as yet, but I'm sure of one thing—that it is painting that brings me true joy, and I am never going to give it up. I felt such relief working on this painting last night that it was almost a therapeutic experience. I do not care if I do not become the most famous painter in the world, or if others are considered better artists than me, or if my paintings do not earn me lacs of rupees, or even if I have to take up another job alongside. All I know is that I am going to do my best and spend as much time painting as I can. I love what I do, and hopefully, sooner or later, others will appreciate it as well."

Hari Master stood up, smiled warmly at his enthusiastic student, and gently running his hands through his hair, said, "Good for you, son. Be persistent, do not become complacent, and always endeavour to strengthen the skills you already have. When you do what you love, and that too whole-heartedly, you are bound to excel at it and your primary reward then, is doing the work itself. Now let us go and try to communicate this to your father. I'll show him the wonderful painting you have made first. I'm sure it will work in our favour."

Finishing his story, Areen sat back, leaning comfortably against the wooden railing behind him, his observant eyes noting with some satisfaction the contemplative expressions of his audience. His story seemed to have appealed to them, touched them in some way. A few quiet moments having passed with each of the boys and girls lost in their own thoughts, Areen announced, "Alright folks, that is it from me, for the time being. I would now like to give you all a chance to speak. But first, take a short break for about an hour to think about and clarify your own feelings regarding what has just been said. Reflect on what it means to you and your own lives. I would suggest that you initially do this by yourselves, and only after that discuss with your friends, if at all you feel the need. But it would be ideal if the sharing begins here with all of us together. Ok then, off you go."

After an hour had passed, the group reassembled before their guide and Areen wasted no time in asking who among them wished to volunteer to speak. This being the first discussion, each of them was hesitant to express his or her point of view. After some gentle coaxing by Areen, Drishti could be seen raising his hand a little, but put it down the moment Areen's gaze fell on him. Areen gave him a compassionate look, and gestured to him to continue.

"Umm... it is quite personal, actually. Do I really have to say what I am feeling?" Drishti asked.

"I would advise you to, Drishti. Trust me, you will not regret it. Do not deny your friends the chance to share your understanding. Believe me, one of the most wonderful things in friendship is to share honestly about yourself." said Areen. Drishti nodded slowly in agreement. Making up his mind, he stood up, went next to Areen and began to speak.

"Well, as I was listening to the story I really felt I could relate to it emotionally. This may sound too grand but... I feel like... like I have reached some kind of an understanding about life after having heard it. Actually, I have a twenty eight year old elder brother, named Rohan. Ever since I was a child, I would notice, much to my envy, how dearly my parents doted on him. He was like one of those irritatingly perfect 'ideal sons' one finds in television soaps—obedient, disciplined, sensitive, you name it. I was always the careless, casual, happy go lucky kind. However, even though his behavior and the attention it got annoyed me at times, I really looked up to him as someone I wanted to emulate. My parents are both software engineers and, as is common practice in most small-town, middle class families, they wanted the both of us to first become engineers and then get admission into big business schools, so that we could eventually get jobs in reputed multinational companies. What connection there is between engineering and management degrees, I am yet to fully understand! But anyway, Rohan, obviously the more brilliant and hard working of the two of us, had quite a good percentage at the end of his engineering college exams. At least for my parents, the obvious next step was filling up forms for the best business schools. There was no discussion on the matter and Rohan was just expected to move on to the next necessary 'stage' of life.

"There was another side to Rohan, though. He loved playing the guitar. His college was in the same city as we lived and, no matter how hectic his study schedule was or how close the examinations were, he did not miss spending time with his beloved instrument. When I look back now, I realize how it brought a glow to his face like few other things did. Nonetheless, all these years, no one in the family considered it to be a possible career option. It was just one of those things one does on the side to 'pass the time,' not 'serious' work."

Drishti paused a little, recollecting the stressful days before Rohan's entrance examinations. "From morning to night, our parents would obsess about his studies, classes and marks. While Rohan toiled away quietly, devoting almost all of his waking hours to study, he never went a day without an hour of playing his guitar. He would often sacrifice his sleep, but never considered skipping his practice.

"As expected, Rohan kept up his gruelling schedule and did rather well in all his exams, going on to complete his MBA from IIM Lucknow. After such glowing academic success, he returned home with a lucrative job offer from a multinational company. So eager were they to have him on board that they even assigned him a branch in our home city. We were all extremely happy for him. Little did we know what he was actually going through inside.

Drishti sighed and continued, "Rohan attended office for exactly six months. Every day I saw him come home at increasingly late hours. He had become extremely quiet; was growing increasingly withdrawn and began to get irritated at the smallest of things. At the time, all of us thought that this was just a phase he was going through and would get adjusted to this new lifestyle in some time. However, it was not as simple as that. He just did not seem interested in anything or anybody. Something seemed to be welling up inside him which he refused to share with anybody. And then, one fine day, it happened! He stunned us all by declaring that he had quit his job."

"You mean he quit by choice?" asked an incredulous Malhar. "Why would he quit such a good job with so many benefits? Most people would give their right arm for a high paying job in an MNC!"

Drishti replied, "That was what shocked all of us at the time. Suddenly, one day, we hear from Rohan, the apple of everybody's eyes, the man everyone in the family was proud of, that he is just not satisfied with his career. Addressing our parents directly for the first time, he went on to tell them that he had made all attempts to live up to their dreams, that he was fully aware of all the emotion and effort that had been painstakingly invested in him, but try as much as he did, there was no way that he could see himself living that kind of a life anymore. His voice rising as he spoke, he said that his exhausting management studies and now his job did not fulfil him and he did not want to continue to 'waste' his life in this manner. My parents and I listened in shocked silence, wondering how to react. Rohan emphasized how his current lifestyle made him feel completely suffocated and he desperately needed to get out of it. After a point my father had had enough, and he told Rohan to stop talking and come back to his senses. My parents were clearly devastated hearing their son talk like this, but Rohan could no longer hold back, giving vent to his frustration. Eventually, the argument grew so heated that Rohan was asked to leave the house. Quite furious himself, at the sudden turn of events, he gladly obliged and walked out.

"Everything had happened so suddenly, I just could not believe it. I was extremely disappointed. I could not believe what my brother had done, how he had effectively betrayed all our dreams, hopes and expectations, especially those of Mother and Father. They had always lavishly showered their affections on him. How could he have taken such a bold step without consulting us even once? Somewhere deep down, nonetheless, there was still a part of me that did not believe that Rohan could behave in a rash or selfish manner. There had to be some other explanation. Now that he was thrown out of the house, things got even worse, as we had no way of knowing what was going on in his mind."

"Where is Rohan now?" asked Ronak with concern.

"He moved in with a friend, in a single room apartment, on the outskirts of the city. I heard from one of his friends that he takes guitar classes at a music school. He also plays at 'Jazz up your life.'"

"That cannot be!" exclaimed Aditi. "I have heard good reports of this new player at that club since the last few months... but his name is Swarit, not Rohan."

"Yes," nodded Drishti, beginning to look a little proud at the enthusiastic reaction from Aditi. "I believe he took another name to avoid further embarrassment for us." He paused and looked at Areen. "You know, I think I can finally make some sense of why Rohan did what he did. All this while, questions such as what exactly happened, why my brother behaved the way he did, why my parents threw him out of the house have been lurking in my heart. I could never understand how he could give up our life of luxurious comfort to live like that. Why on earth did he choose such a risky profession in comparison to the cushy job he had?" Drishti shook his head in dismay, pouring his heart out now. "And all the pain my parents went through! I swore to myself that I would never forgive my brother for any of that. No matter how much I missed him, I would never speak to him again.

"I think I can understand his perspective now. I can actually sense what he must have felt, what he must have dealt with." He sat with his face cast downwards, trying somehow to rub the tears from his eyes.

Areen carefully responded, "Drishti, we can see how difficult all this has been for you. Well, since you are so overwhelmed by these emotions, why don't you just give your brother a call and let him know how you feel now? Wouldn't you like to know how he feels as well?"

Drishti looked up with a ray of hope on his face and said hesitantly, "Yeah, I think that's a great suggestion. I feel like I have so much to say to him right now. Having shared my experience with everyone else has given me great relief. I feel much lighter now and can speak freely to Rohan. All our wonderful memories of togetherness are coming back to me already."

His excited face grew downcast again as he suddenly remembered, "Oh no! There is no network here. How can I call him?"

Areen smiled and said, "You forget, we do have a land line in the office. Go, make the call right now."

Grinning, Drishti jumped to his feet and ran towards the office.

The others, who too had, to different degrees, got involved, in Drishti's story, began to cheer for him enthusiastically. Some even began to clap and whistle. Drishti's roller coaster emotions had got them all engaged empathetically and they were all very eager that the two brothers make peace.

While he was gone, the boys began an animated discussion among themselves, wondering how Rohan would respond to this sudden offer of an olive branch. Everyone was waiting impatiently for Drishti's return.

Drishti was back after nearly half an hour, visibly delighted and grinning from ear to ear. "I cannot even begin to tell you how happy I am. Can you believe it! I just spoke to my brother for a whole half hour! There was no bitterness on Rohan's part. In fact, he immediately told me how he often thinks of me and our parents and longs for all of us to be together. I asked him how he was doing with regard to his career. The first few months were incredibly tough and uncertain, he said. He had to live off his friends' money for almost a year and really had to watch his expenses to adapt to a way of life he was completely unaccustomed to.

Alongside, the emotional turmoil of separating from the family had provoked a great deal of introspection. After a lot of soul searching, he finally realized that what he had been looking for was not all that difficult to find. It was right there in front of him, but he had been unable to see it. All through his lonely and depressing days, the one constant relaxation had been his daily ritual with his guitar. This was something he knew he really cared about and enjoyed, and would be eagerly willing to spend all his energies doing. It really was as simple as that. Soon, he was clear in his mind that the joy he derived from playing the guitar all day was more valuable to him than anything else. He then set out patiently to enhance his skills and devoted himself to this activity for a good six months. Having built up his confidence enough to feel ready to look for a job, he started by playing in small local bars. Often, the stint was for less than ten minutes. On a few occasions, he even played his guitar on the streets, just to earn enough to get through the day. Gradually, after another six months of searching, he got the job at the school and the club gig. He says he has been quite fortunate to now have many interested students with whom he has built a relationship of genuine affection. The club performances are being appreciated too. Even though he does not earn as much as he would have, had he continued his job, at that multinational, he really sounds content with his life. There was such excitement and enthusiasm in his voice as he spoke about his job. It really was thrilling to hear that he is well settled and at peace with himself. We have even decided to meet as soon as we can, and speak to our parents about all that has happened, so that the whole family can get back together as soon as possible. I am sure they will be very pleased to learn that he has made such progress."

Drishti finally paused a little and shook his head in wonderment. "I am so proud of him. He sounded so humble and yet so confident and committed. Wow!"

Areen was quite pleased at how sensitively his student had bothered to respond to his story. He offered the crystal that he had pulled out of his Box at the beginning of the story to Drishti, who looked at its beautiful colours in admiration. "A labradorite! Look how the colours keep changing when one holds it at different angles."

Areen nodded with a smile, "Yes. Keep it safely. You can look upon it as a reminder that we often need to see things in a fresh light."

Drishti agreed and thanked him with sincere gratitude. Now self-conscious with all the attention, he settled awkwardly into a corner and tried to melt into the background. "Could you please continue the game Areen?" he pleaded.

"Certainly!" Areen clapped his hands together lightly and slipped back into his role of raconteur.

It was time for the next tale.

2

Auditions for the annual beauty contest, at college, would be underway within an hour. Alishia swept her long hair back gracefully, angling her face first one way and then the other, and examined her makeup with satisfaction. Delighted at how stunning she looked, she smiled and moved away from the mirror with graceful confidence.

Poor Anita doesn't stand a chance, she thought to herself. 'The lead role belongs to me.'

Alishia was accustomed to being centrestage in life and had no intentions of allowing it to be any different on this particular platform. Besides, as one of the most popular girls in college, it was almost a given. Surely, she did not need to worry. Alongside these thoughts of confidence, however, there also lurked a considerable amount of fear and doubt. How embarrassing it would be, if someone else got the role. What if Anita actually gets through and I don't? How will I ever go back to college again after that… These thoughts did affect Alishia, but so blinded was she by her desire to be the best, so anxious was she to win each contest she participated in, that she did not pay attention to them, dismissing them as signs of weakness.

On her way to college, she recalled how, as a beautiful child, she would receive compliments on a routine basis. It all started in class eight. The annual school event featured a classical waltz dance, for which she was chosen without even an audition, just because of how pretty she was. The selection had felt a little strange at first, but once all the congratulations and admiration from others in class began, her feelings of self-doubt began to dissipate. If so many people, including the class teacher, had appreciated her for something, it must be true. What a lovely feeling it was to get all that attention. It made one feel so much more special than everybody else.

From that day on, two things became paramount in Alishia's life, her beautiful appearance, and winning. Alishia made it a point to resolutely try for as many school events as she could. Any extra-curricular activity, whether it be dancing or a beauty contest, Alishia would not only participate, but go to all lengths possible to ensure her victory. First place was what mattered, and that was what everyone was after. Getting there was important, irrespective of the means one used. Those who made it were praised, while the others had to make do with being ordinary. This was the motivation that got her fired up, and had led to a lot of past accomplishments and awards. This same motivation had made her participate in the forthcoming beauty contest.

Despite how effortless and continuous, a rise to the top, it seemed, to any outsider, there were hidden scars that Alishia had had to suffer in the process; secrets only Alishia knew of and could not dare tell anyone.

From being a carefree, happy-go-lucky child, she had transformed into an excessively self-conscious and anxious teenager. Constant worrying was now part of her everyday life. After all, it was so hard to please everyone. Weight was a major concern and every morsel had to be judged for the extra kilos it brought to her waist rather than how nourishing it was. Hairstyles and colours had to repeatedly be adjusted to meet the latest trends. Clothes, shoes and accessories were each a whole new subject of study. Makeup required heavy investment. And if all that was not enough, learning by rote certain profound answers to keep up the appearance of being intelligent was also a requirement for this 'perfect' person Alishia was trying to mould herself into. Life as one of the perennial local beauty queens was no easy task.

The tougher part however was the compromises she made with her heart—the shrewdness with which she befriended the 'right' people, the calculating ways in which she used her charms to gain access to whatever she wanted. She recalled her parting friends' last words, *We were friends for so long, Alishia. We know you too well for you to fool us. It's obvious you are embarrassed by us now because we are too simple and uninterested in keeping up with the new façade you have decided to put on. Don't bother denying it. All these games you play. By the time you realize who your true friends are, it might be too late.* They walked off with a sad look, and although she told herself she had brushed it aside, the pain of them leaving like this, stayed in her heart.

Her last boyfriend had voiced similar warnings when they had broken up. *Alishia, do you even realize what you are doing? You have chosen to surround yourself with fair- weather friends who, more than anything else, are interested in what advantage you can be to them; that is why they keep praising you and even though you say you can see through it, you often cannot. Wake up from your delusion before it is too late!*

The car braked abruptly and Alishia was jolted out of her daydreams, back into the present. The moment she got down, she, almost automatically now out of habit, pasted a fake smile on her face and waved indifferently to some enthusiastic, admiring boys. The past seemed to weigh down on her as she tapped her high heels along the campus courtyard. Distracted as she was by her thoughts, she stumbled slightly on the way and her mobile went flying out of her hand. Instinctively lunging for it, she lost her balance completely and crashed straight into the girl seated under the banyan tree, engrossed in reading her books.

As both of them recovered from the sudden collision and straightened themselves up, the girl said to Alishia with a smile, "Am I so magnetic a personality?"

The joke was witty and Alishia almost blurted out laughing, but then realized that this person was a complete stranger and that she was actually supposed to get angry in such situations. She also went on to notice that, much to her dismay, her heels had broken, her bracelet had snapped and her handbag strap had torn at the shoulder. That made her even more furious. These were accessories she could not bear to lose, as she believed they greatly accentuated her beauty. How terrible she would look without them, and how would she get all the appreciation she was so used to? There was still the whole day to spend in college. She could not go home early because there were important tests to take that day. Tears of frustration welled up in her eyes. As she attempted to wipe them off, disappointment struck again and she found marks of her blue eyeliner all over her fingers. So overwhelmed was she by all this, so huge a value did she place on these things, that she sank down exhausted and silent.

Wondering what it was that had made Alishia so upset, the girl asked, "Are you alright? Did you hurt yourself? I was only joking..."

Having someone right in front of her, to witness all that she was going through was, for Alishia, the last straw. Upset with herself for being so careless, she covered her face with her hands and began to sob silently. A couple of people close by came up to ask what the matter was, but the other girl quickly waved them away.

Once they were alone, the girl asked again, "Look, are you sure you are not hurt?"

Alishia was sitting quietly now, her hair covering much of her face. She nodded numbly. Thoughts of missing out on the audition were racing through her mind. How am I going to make it for the audition now? The very idea of tottering in on broken heels, looking like a complete mess, makes me sick. This is such a nightmare! How I wish I could just disappear right now...

"I can't believe this has happened!" she shouted out aloud. For someone as concerned about appearances as Alishia, this was quite literally a moment of hitting ground-zero.

"What can't you believe? Aren't you glad you have fallen for me?" she joked again, trying to lighten things up.

Reacting sharply to that comment, Alishia darted a furious look her way, but the girl did not take it too seriously and handed her a handkerchief to clean her tear-stricken, eyeliner smudged face. Alishia reluctantly accepted the proffered peace offering.

"I am going to be late for this very important beauty contest audition," she complained. "Even if I get there now, I don't think it's going to matter. And you are not as funny as you think! Who are you anyway? Why are you acting so concerned about me? Do I even know you?"

Her new friend, on the other hand, was relieved to hear that this was all there was to the problem. From the look on Alishia's face, she had been worried if Alishia had hurt her head in the fall and had suffered some kind of trauma. "Ok, ok, my jokes were out of line, sorry. And you may not recognize me, but of course I know you, Alishia. We are in the same class, B.A. (Honours) English, second year, in case you have forgotten! My name is Sonali," said the girl smiling.

While Alishia was a little taken aback at how Sonali could be so comfortable with someone from the same class not recognizing her and wondered if she had any self-respect at all, Sonali extended her hand out to her for a handshake. Alishia, however, thought she was trying to help her up and in the bargain, stumbled again unsteadily. A sharp pain in her ankle made her wince and she swore under her breath. Leaning on Sonali, she cried out in disgust, "I think I have sprained my ankle." Sitting down on the ground, she examined her ankle closely. "Just when things couldn't get any worse. There goes my annual show!" she said, cursing her misfortune.

Sonali too, had a look at the ankle. Mildly surprised at Alishia's reaction on having hurt herself, she commented, "It clearly is swollen. But you seem more concerned about your audition than your own well being."

This observation brought back Alishia's morning ruminations with fresh stabs of pain. Before she could realize what she was saying, she blurted out, "But that is the only way one's existence matters! What is the point of doing anything if one isn't better than everybody else? How will people recognize me if I am not the star of the show? College life is a precursor of one's life to come, is it not? If I fail here, I will surely fail later as well! I have to make every opportunity count."

Sonali could only raise her eyebrows at this dramatic conclusion. She pulled out a crepe bandage from her backpack and with expert movements began to tape the swollen ankle. "How come you have a bandage?" Alishia asked in surprise.

Sonali replied, "I am in the college theatre society. We practically live in college the whole day and so are prepared for everything."

"You are in the theatre society?" Alishia asked rather brusquely, with a puzzled look on her face. "But I have never seen you in any of the plays performed in the auditorium?"

"Yes, I am into sound, design and lights. My name just gets announced at the end in the credits which nobody pays attention to," she said laughing casually. "But I am very proud to be part of our group. Our team has won a lot of appreciation from a number of respected theatre experts in the country."

"What do you mean 'won appreciation'? What does that amount to? You mean you have won a huge number of awards in a lot of inter-collegiate theatre competitions, right?" asked a slightly confused Alishia. "Wow! So you must be really popular then?"

Sonali replied, "Well, I suppose not. You didn't know me, did you? And we are in the same class!"

Alishia felt a little guilty on hearing this but tried to cover up. "Well, I have been very busy with all my competitions, you know. You may have seen my snaps in the college magazine and of course, in the *City Times* and a couple of other papers," she said, trying to adopt a nonchalant attitude, while inwardly glowing with pride at her fame.

"Sure, I have," said Sonali, "and you are looking rather nice in all of them too. We have some group photographs with our awards in that magazine too."

In no mood for polite formality, Alishia asked impulsively, "But why do you speak of your achievements in such a casual way? Are you not proud of them? And why are you into theatre at all, if your work is not highlighted and receives no mention, except at the end for a few moments? Does that not bother you? Doesn't it make all your efforts rather pointless?"

Mildly amused at Alishia's outburst, Sonali answered back, "Hey! Calm down, calm down. Of course, I like to win awards or see my photograph in the college magazine or the newspaper. When did I say I did not? But beyond a point, it does not really matter. Actually, and I'm not being boastful here, our theatre society functions quite differently from how most other extra-curricular activity societies run. And whatever it is, I am quite comfortable with my place in it. In fact, strange as it may sound, we do not believe in competition actually..."

"What?" exclaimed Alishia, utterly surprised, "How can that be? And how have you won all these awards then?" She was speechless. For as long as she could remember, competition had been her motivating force, something that had defined her way of life.

"Yes, we do participate in competitions when other colleges hold them. But right since its inception, our theatre society has organized 'festivals,' not 'competitions.' Our staff-advisor is of the view, that, generally speaking, a competition is built up or arranged in such a way, that it ends up promoting a spirit of one-upmanship among its participants, prioritizing working *against* one another over working towards the higher goal of the pursuit of excellence in the field. We all have come to agree with him. Putting its participants into positions where they cannot share ideas freely, a competition discourages honest analysis of another's work, and even one's own.

"To avoid this kind of a setup, what we do in our festivals, and encourage others to do as well, is that after the performances of all the groups are over, we all sit down together for a rigorous discussion of the positive and negative points of each group. Everybody is welcome to participate in this discussion, including the audience members. It often goes on until late at night, even one o'clock at times. Sometimes there are heated arguments and harsh criticisms, but there is also heartfelt collective approval and praise, all of which are especially looked forward to if they come from reputed stalwarts in the field. This way, at the end of the day, each one goes away having learnt more about how he could improve as a theatre person..."

Alishia had been listening attentively, but she had genuinely believed in a particular approach to life for many years and could not accept Sonali's novel ideas so easily. "But don't competitions motivate one to do better than everyone else and, in that way, excel in one's field? How would one know who is better at something, if there were no competitions? And don't you feel excited, when it is announced that your group is the winner among those competing? Surely, you cannot deny that. I feel really exhilarated about it and I am not ashamed to say so. When I won last year's annual college beauty contest for instance, I cannot begin to tell you how delighted I felt standing on that stage receiving my trophy and prize money. The adulation I got after the event, not only from friends, but even from complete strangers in college, was the icing on the cake. That feeling is incomparable, and undoubtedly worth striving for!"

"You are right. One does feel exhilarated on such occasions. But shouldn't one be careful about how much value one attaches to such feelings? If you really think about it, what does such a victory really mean—that you can do better than the few people around you on a particular day? It does not tell you much more than that, does it? If you must compete, compete with yourself. That is what requires more courage and is a far more valuable achievement. We try to nurture such an attitude within our group. Though we elect a society President from among us, and three student heads as members, from first, second and third year, we also firmly believe that everyone has a voice which deserves to be heard. All of us recognize the importance of cooperation and working together, respect each other's contribution and do the best we can for our group to flourish. After all, if even one person in the chain was missing, how would the performance be put up? Who would do that person's job and who is to say with finality whether it is more or less valuable than the tasks assigned to others? Sure, as in any group, there are some people who stand out and are more talented than others. However, that does not give them the license to be vain, and Sir especially makes sure of that. Doing the best each of us could do at a given point of time, that is our group's principal inspiration; and when we look back on a play that went off well, we cherish the moments we spent together, as a team, working on it. That is what primarily matters to us, rather than gloating over the number of people we managed to defeat.

"Also, since you've brought it up... About these beauty contests, you know... I personally feel the merits of such events are quite questionable and certainly not what the media makes it out to be. Sure, the winners are known all over the world, they get a lot of money, and who wouldn't want all that. But finally, apart from what the sponsors of these contests gift them, what really is their achievement? I mean, what do they really mean by 'beauty' in these contests anyway? Has someone even seriously thought about that? Is being beautiful only about being of a particular height, weight or complexion with a superficial knowledge of current affairs? Is that all? I really don't get it...

"I used to be quite enamored of such contests and the women who win them, when I had first entered college. But now I am not. Once I began to wonder about what goes on behind the scenes, I began to think quite differently. What good do these contests do for the world anyway? If anything, they distort the values of those who are blinded by glamour, erode their self-esteem and create all kinds of insecurities. At least in our plays, we attempt to raise important concerns about life, create awareness about them and make whatever little difference we can in the world..."

Suddenly noticing the flummoxed expression on Alishia's face and realizing that the person she was speaking to was on her way to participate in such an event, Sonali stopped herself from going further on with her tirade.

"Hey, sorry! I just don't understand these things, that is why the outburst. Forgive me for going on endlessly. I have a tendency to not stop talking once I start," she said smiling good-naturedly.

Alishia pretended to laugh it all off to keep up appearances, but what she had just heard had stirred her inside, quite strongly.

Sonali's could also see that some of what she had said had made Alishia think. Immediately, she remembered her first days in the theatre society when her teacher's words would leave her wondering, with a similar expression on her face. Perhaps some of the things she had learnt there, over the years, had become so much a part of her that they just effortlessly came up even in casual conversation. But not everyone wanted to discuss such things, she knew. Not wanting to press Alishia too much on the matter, fearing it would make her defensive and seem like she wanted to put her down, Sonali quickly excused herself from the place saying, "Hey! I got so involved in our conversation that I forgot about some work Sir had asked me to do. Sorry for leaving so abruptly, but I have to rush. It was really nice meeting you, take care, and good luck." Saying so, she ran off in the direction of the auditorium, with Alishia mumbling a meek but sincere, "Goodbye, nice meeting you!" in response.

With Sonali's departure, Alishia was now left alone with her thoughts, 'Look at how relaxed and self-assured this girl is. How 'free' she seems to be, how comfortable with who she is, with what she feels, with what she believes, with how she talks, what she wears… with just about everything. She is not out to impress anyone, she is not torturing herself each second of the day to win some 'rat race' so that she can be proud of herself. And look at me! Doing all the opposite things and worrying endlessly over them… Where has it brought me? There was such warmth, such affection in the way she met me, even though it was for the first time. And she genuinely wanted to help me. There was no ulterior motive. How refreshing it is to meet someone like that! Can one truly live without lying to oneself or forcing oneself to deny things one likes? Sonali does not seem to have repressed any of her genuine feelings or desires in choosing what she has. She actually seems to be content with it. And she had mentioned how earlier she was quite like me... how then did she change so drastically?'

Reflecting on the thoughts of her past that had been bedevilling her since morning, as well as what she had just heard from Sonali, Alishia walked along the college corridor aimlessly, when a poster on the adjacent wall caught her eye, 'Auditions for *Theatrics*, the theatre society of Maharana Pratap College, begin today. Those interested, please report to the auditorium by 1:30 pm.'

Alishia looked at her watch, it was one o'clock. Her ankle was much better now and she could go up to the senior student, who conducted the beauty contest audition and persuade her to wait for her while she went back home and changed. However, having looked thoughtfully at the poster for several minutes, she smiled to herself thinking, Why not? After a brief stop at the nearest restroom to remove all her makeup, she made her way to the auditorium. Going by the lightness in her step, she seemed to be quite at ease with herself.

∽

The story over, Areen now waited patiently before starting to speak. As he observed his students' expressions, each of them lost in their own thoughts, he drew from his 'Box of Tales' a key chain attached to a tiny diary. This one had an attractively designed cover, but as Areen flipped its pages, one could see that they were all pitch black.

I wonder why anyone would keep a diary like that, thought Aditi to herself.

"Well," said Areen, "As you had done earlier, take a break for about an hour and think about the story. The discussion will be open to all of you when we meet. Whoever wants to volunteer to speak, and this time I am sure there will be a few, is welcome to do so and we will take it forward from there. See you then."

Each of the friends went their separate ways to ruminate on their responses to what they had heard. When they returned after the allotted time, Aditi was the first to raise her hand and ask, "Your story was interesting indeed, Areen, but don't you think it ended rather uncertainly? Why did you not go on to tell us what happened to Alishia after she decided to go for the auditions? The stories we are used to hearing or reading, don't usually end this way. When they are over, they leave one with the feeling that all questions that were initially raised, have been satisfactorily answered, and the lives of most, if not all the characters the readers are introduced to, come to some kind of closure. Though your story did engage us all throughout your narration, this one aspect seemed to me to be a bit odd."

Pleased that she had been paying attention, Areen replied, "Good observation, Aditi. I am sure many of you must have felt the same way, but hesitated to ask. Well, you are right. I do prefer open-ended stories to others because they seem to be truer to life. I do not think that one's life necessarily offers us neat, tied-up endings. Not all the problems one started out with, are solved and not all questions answered. One neither feels that all the good one did in this life has been rewarded, nor that the wrongs one did or suffered, has been paid for, corrected or forgiven. In fact, to my mind, at no point in life can one really say that all one's trials and tribulations are over and from now on, *everything* would work according to one's design and plan. The attempt to control life such that a sweet, 'happily-ever-after' outcome is guaranteed is a popular, but misguided, aspiration fuelled especially these days by the heavily commercialised self help industry. The truth is that life continues to happen with each day being a new day, that confronts us with new situations, both good and bad. One must therefore learn to make conscious choices again and again. To respond with awareness to every new situation that comes one's way.

"Leaving a story unfinished this way helps recreate this important aspect of life for the listeners or readers, something that a closed-ended story does not do. So, I did not go on to say what Alishia's future would be, because I wished to emphasize that it will depend primarily on the choices she herself makes at different stages of her life. Does that make things a bit clearer?"

Aditi nodded and sat back thoughtfully, mulling over what Areen had just said. Meanwhile, Swapnil joined in with a question of his own. "The story was thought-provoking indeed, Areen. Despite what it said about competitions in it, I was just wondering, don't people often themselves want to outdo each other or succeed at someone else's cost, as long as it gets them what they want? Why then blame competitions for such behavior? Moreover, why should someone who is more talented than the others, not be rewarded or treated accordingly? That is his right, is it not?"

Sheetal stated her opinion even more candidly. "Frankly speaking, I disagree with some of the ideas expressed in the story, Areen," she said, with clear annoyance in her voice. She seemed to have been personally insulted as she continued, "You know, I am sorry to have to say this, but I think it a matter of pride for girls to be beautiful, and for boys to be handsome. I am proud of being thought of as beautiful, and do not see any harm in it. I think it is a natural gift that a few special people are given and they should cherish its benefits. What is the harm in that? And what can we do if others do not have the gifts that we have? It is not our fault. Also, is one not naturally attracted to someone who is beautiful? Who among us could deny that? I feel it is a bit hypocritical to pretend that this is not true."

There were a few moments of complete silence when she finished, as the two people who dared to question the profound wisdom of the 'all-knowing' Areen, aroused great awe among their companions.

Areen, for his part, took his time to collect his thoughts, and then replied, "Very good Swapnil and Sheetal, I am glad you voiced what you were thinking, even though it somewhat goes against what the story seems to say. Swapnil, you are right. Often, people themselves are responsible for such behavior and it is not only in competitions that one gets to see it. However, in the story I told you, Sonali's criticism is directed at the significant extent to which the very framework or format of a competition, the design itself, induces people to turn against one another, when they are placed within it. That is what she wishes to challenge.

She wants us to recognize the benefits of cooperation instead of competition."

Having made the first of his points, Areen paused for a minute just to check if his audience was tuned in to him or he was going too fast for them. "With me so far? Does anyone else have something to say about the story, or what Swapnil and Sheetal have said?" Noticing that most members of the group were engrossed in listening to him and did not seem to want to say anything at this point, he continued, "Alright. Coming to the other issues that the two of you have raised, well, Swapnil and Sheetal, I understand why you believe what you said about talent and beauty. But I would like you to consider another point of view. For me, there is more merit in an individual placing value on what he can achieve through his efforts, rather than passively exploiting something he was simply fortunate enough to have. As old-fashioned, outdated and clichéd as it may sound, I believe there is some truth in this statement. At the end of the day, the value addition that you bring in through your own efforts, is what will give you lasting satisfaction. Nobody can take that away from you, no matter what they do, and you can rest with the confidence that you have earned this yourself. It is nice to occasionally have something gifted to us by chance, who would mind that; but what significance and sense of worth you can really derive from it in the long run, is debatable.

"As regards talent, a lovely line from one of John Donne's poems comes to mind, *No man is an island*. It would be prudent to remind ourselves of something we so conveniently overlook—the innumerable factors around us that we are influenced and supported by. Any achievement is never one person's doing alone.

Who knows, perhaps the daily wage labourer who helped build my house, could have performed as well, or even better than me, if he had been given the same facilities and opportunities as I was. The circumstances one is born into, and what they make available to one, clearly play a huge role in the matter—one's parents' own culture, understanding and mindset, what kind of an education they could afford for their child, for how long they could afford it to help him further refine already existing skills or to help cultivate new skills—these are no small concerns.

"Consider the stories we know of now famous actors or actresses, writers, painters or cricketers who were spotted on the streets by sheer accident and then given the required opportunities for them to grow. The emphasis in these stories is often laid on the fact, of how someone rose from rags to riches, from anonymity to stardom, due to sheer hard work and perseverance. But, the question of what would have happened to him if he was not spotted by a senior expert in the field, on a particular day, is rarely raised.

"Similarly, the case for beauty is even harder to defend, I would say. Always appearing beautiful does takes some maintenance, but I doubt if it's the kind of preparation required to nurture talents such as those I just mentioned..."

Malhar raised his hand to add to the discussion and Areen gestured to him to speak. "I have something to say about this, Areen! The story and Sheetal's question both reminded me of this documentary I saw once on how in many parts of the world, the features people think of as 'beautiful,' are very different from the ones we would associate with beauty. The topic aroused my interest quite a bit and I racked my brains for a long time over 'what it means to be beautiful?' But it did not lead me to any concrete answers, so I let it go..."

Areen responded: "That is true, Malhar, there are indeed societies in the world whose definitions of beauty are quite different from what we are used to. One would find this to be true not only across the world, but even within different parts of India. In fact, I was just reading a novel set in the late 1900s apartheid South Africa, which made me think about the fascination with fair skin in our country. Interestingly, in this book, a young black boy describes the features of a white American woman with blonde hair, which most of us here would consider beautiful, as ugly! He prefers the features of black women instead.

"Note however, that the existence of more than one conception of beauty, should not make one do away with the idea of beauty altogether and pronounce that nothing really is beautiful. Different cultures have different ideas of beauty and what needs to be understood is that it is a subjective quality and not an absolute. So, in this sense, beauty does indeed lie in the eye of the beholder! Sheetal is right when she says there is no harm in feeling happy about being beautiful and the appreciation one gets for it. However, unless tempered with this knowledge and its consequent humility, there is a danger of becoming vain or obsessed with such appreciation. Sure, one can be grateful for it and enjoy it for what it is, but to imagine that being beautiful or attractive makes one 'superior' to others in some way would surely be to delude oneself. Be careful of that."

Saying so, Areen quietly handed over his key-chain diary to Sheetal. "Here, keep this with you. I used it to remind myself of the old adage, *Never judge a book by its cover*! Appearances can often be deceptive. For all its attractiveness, this little diary offers no value to its owner–its pages are unusable."

A little reluctant at first, she eventually trusted the guide's wisdom and accepted it.

With enough time having been spent on the current discussion, Areen decided to move forward. "Alright, that was great. I am happy that quite a few of you voiced your concerns and participated in the discussion. We will break for half an hour now and then start with the next story."

When the group assembled again, Areen was ready to begin anew.

3

Raahi threw his pen down on the desk in exasperation. It was already 6.30 a.m. Bleary eyed, he reached for his cup of coffee. 'Barely a few hours left to finish the report. Sleep is out of the question. If I don't hand this in on time, the boss won't be able to make his presentation to the parent company board. That would be disastrous... I could lose my job today!' he thought, shaking himself awake, as tried to focus again.

This had been a pattern that had never really left Raahi, or rather, a pattern that he had not left since the last several years. Through most of his college days, his work was incomplete until the deadline was looming dangerously close, but his brilliance had always helped him get by, somehow. A skilled debater, he would casually dismiss any advice others gave him, regarding improving any aspect of his personality by saying, "That is the way it works for me. I work best under pressure." Priding himself on his ability to argue cogently, he could summon so many reasons to support his views that it took little time for him to believe that he was right and others were not; and though he did not state it overtly, he had long decided, he did not need other people with mediocre minds to tell him who he was and how he should behave. He was answerable only to himself and none else. He had begun to cultivate such an attitude in his early years in college, when he had genuinely faced unfair criticism from people who were threatened by his capabilities. At that time, there had been no other choice but to aggressively stand up for himself. Little did he realize, however, that his reasoning had long since derailed from aiming for objectivity to self-justification and rationalization of his own actions. Thirty years old now, he had reached a stage where so convinced was he of his righteousness, that he did not even try doing things any other way. The result was that Raahi had never completed any task, personal or professional, with time to spare.

By the time he was done with his MBA, he had become adept at (what he called) multitasking. So it was not uncommon to find him juggling various commitments at the same time. He would boast to his friends, "One should always try to utilize one's time as well as one can. I can read my emails while texting SMSs on the phone, I can listen to my girlfriend while simultaneously compiling sales reports, I can read a book while watching television... That is the only way to cope with all the pressure I am under, and simultaneously accomplish a lot too." These were all tall claims, and it was obvious to everybody, but him, that the more his attention was divided, the less he could concentrate on his work and the more mistakes he made. Consequently, he had even begun to leave simple tasks and errands incomplete and overdue. His secretary spent half her time reminding him of approaching deadlines. He would be late for most of his appointments and apologize and fumble through scheduled discussions, promising to come prepared the next time, a promise he never kept.

Ultimately, the inevitable happened. His slack behavior was no longer acceptable to his boss. "You know how professional the new European owners are Raahi. For all the brilliance you may have, this will no longer work. I cannot keep covering up for you. They will not stand for this careless attitude. You had better clean up your act or you know how severe the consequences can be." The project he was currently working on was assigned to him right after this firm warning and he could not afford any blunders this time.

The next thing Raahi could hear was his phone ringing out aloud and, uttering a loud curse, he woke up with a start. He received the call and said *Hello* only to hear his boss spew out venom angrily.

"This is the height of irresponsibility, Raahi! Where the hell are you? It is ten thirty and you still have not arrived. There is no point now because the meeting was scheduled at ten o' clock and our clients have left, disappointed with our work ethic. You are not fit to be part of this company. We are a leading brand in our industry and we take pride in the high standards we have maintained so far. No man worth his salt would be so careless about his commitments. Have you ever heard of a leader who failed to keep his word or was ever late for an appointment? Never! You know what... You may not deliver what you promise, but I will. I told you this was your last chance. Consider yourself fired."

That was it. His boss had disconnected the call and Raahi had just been officially thrown out of his job. He was upset about it indeed, but after the initial sulk was over, all he could think of was how 'the world was always against him' rather than using the moment to introspect on what he had done wrong. He was at a loss as to what he should do with himself. He considered going into the office to retrieve his things but decided against it. What if good sense dawns on my boss and he calls me back? Better to wait awhile for him to cool off, he consoled himself.

Towards the evening, his optimism had begun to wane. Feeling the need to talk to someone, he called his girlfriend in the hope of hearing a few sympathetic words of support.

"Hi Manisha, Listen to me. Something unbelievable has happened. I must talk to you about it..."

"Hello Raahi... I am so grateful you finally found the time to call me... Even I had something important to discuss with you, and I know you are a very busy man, but I really need to go first this time."

"But Manisha I just..."

"Raahi, when I saw your number on my mobile right now, a part of me was hoping you had called because you were missing me and wanted to apologize... But as soon as I picked up and you said you had something to discuss, I immediately scolded myself for being so foolish. Raahi, do you even remember that we have not spoken for an entire week? It is true we do that often when we fight, but you just forgot about me now, don't you? Did it even strike you once that three days ago was the anniversary of the day you had first proposed to me, an occasion we had promised to celebrate together every year! Last year you said you had some important work-related trip to go on, and it would not happen again. Do you have any idea how much it hurt me and how much I had cried when, of all things, you completely 'forgot' all about it this time as well? I am fed up of always being the one to have to understand you, Raahi. Time and again, I have patiently tolerated waiting for calls that you promised to make, standing around at movie halls or restaurants wondering if you will make it in time and vacations being postponed to suit your convenience. I had even told you the last time we fought, how unimportant and taken for granted you had been making me feel. You had, as usual promised to change but did not. I have had enough now, especially after last week. I realize that I am only deceiving myself, expecting you to improve..."

Raahi was stunned by this unexpected turn of events. Manisha was supposed to sympathize with him, not berate him like this. "Don't do this Manisha, stop, please... I just lost my job! I have been under so much pressure that I could not finish that project I was working on and..."

"I am sorry to hear that, Raahi," Manisha replied coldly, "I had been warning you about this for the longest time. It was bound to happen. I know you and, try as I might, I cannot sympathize with you. You are irresponsible and self-centered. Whatever you had so far, came too easily. You never valued it because you did not have to struggle for it. You had more than enough time to complete that project, I know that for a fact. But as usual, you probably started working on it only a few days ago, right? Get over your overconfidence and carelessness and face the truth before it is too late, Raahi! Time waits for no one. And I won't be waiting for you anymore either. There is nothing more for me to say. We will not be meeting again, so do not try to get in touch with me now. Goodbye, and best wishes for your future."

Raahi could not believe what he had just heard. He had been hoping for a much softer stance than this. "Come on, Manisha! I just lost my job! I am supposed to be one of the best at doing what I do, and I was sacked! I was aiming for the Asia region position. Do you know how hard this is to take? Can't you… "

Raahi was only speaking to himself now; there was no one else on the line. What a day this was turning out to be. Losing both his job and his girlfriend in a matter of a few hours—it was too bad to be true.

Lost in a fresh bout of self pity, he was still too self-absorbed to pay attention to what Manisha had just said to him or to realize the extent of distress he had caused her. Eventually, fed up with the disturbing events of the day, he decided to take a walk in the park close to his house, to calm himself down.

He reached the park but was still feeling too low and emotionally drained to exert himself. Collapsing on the first empty bench he could find, he observed the others exercising around him with some contempt. Look at these people running around trying to keep fit. What a joke! I can see some of them have rushed over directly from their offices. They have no time for themselves and even their leisure has become such a stressful, rushed affair. At least I have a chance to sit back and relax now.'

His old defence mechanism was back at work and, as usual, he had begun to rationalize his current situation to suit himself. My boss is only concerned with profit. That selfish man never bothered about my welfare even though I toiled so hard for him… My God, I cannot even remember when I last had the free time to sit in a park like this. I stayed up the whole of last night working and this was not the first time I have done so. Yet, after all that effort, he fires me. What an ingrate! Who needs an exploitative job like that? Even the salary was really not in keeping with my worth. To hell with them. Even if he comes back begging now, I will refuse to join him. With all my experience behind me, something better is bound to come my way. And, just like that, any faint guilt about slacking in work or any desire to be reinstated, had quickly disappeared. Everything seemed 'crystal clear', as it were.

As he smiled in pride and straightened his shoulders, a friendly exclamation from out of nowhere surprised him. "Raahi… Raahi Saxena? Is that really you? Good lord, it must have been at least ten years since we last met!"

Raahi looked up to find his old college classmate, Mohit, standing right before him with his hands on his hips and a delighted expression on his face. For a moment, Raahi was nonplussed by Mohit's smile, recalling him to be the quiet, simple bespectacled nerd of the class, who always occupied the first bench. Mohit's marks had often come close to Raahi's top ranking scores. However, Raahi had always thought himself better than Mohit, because, in his opinion, he put in less than half the effort that Mohit did. He remembered that Mohit had seemed friendly enough at that time, but Raahi had always suspected that he secretly envied him as much as the others did.

Mohit seemed to carry none of the burden of this past, and went on speaking happily, "It's so wonderful to see you, Raahi! How have you been? Do you live nearby? Last I heard you were flying off to Europe every month? Is that true? Are you settled there now?"

Already in an irritable state of mind, Raahi held up his hands defensively to slow down the barrage of questions fired at him. "Take it easy, Mohit! Yes, I know it's been a while. A lot has happened since then..." He went quiet abruptly, not knowing what to say next, wondering how to avoid the embarrassment of disclosing his current condition. Deciding to buy himself some time, he asked Mohit, "I have been doing well. But what about you? What are you up to these days?"

Taking this as an invitation to join Raahi on the bench, much to the latter's discomfort, Mohit began talking, "Oh, you know how it is, Raahi. I did not get into Ahmedabad as you did, but I did make it to Jamshedpur for the MBA. Subsequently, I was lucky enough to get a great placement in an IT company with which I stayed for a good 8 years, ending up as their HR head for the Asia Region. But then Vandana, my wife, wanted us to shift here, to be close to her aging parents. My parents stay with my brother, so I could understand her cause for worry, and decided to quit and find a new job here. The organization is relatively new but it is growing at a fast pace and my position is decent. The pay is not as good, but it is exciting work. We live just on the other side of this park and are still getting used to this city. But that is enough about me. Tell me what's up with you buddy? Is yours a German concern? Or Swedish? I forget what I had heard..."

Raahi had been listening with a mix of bewilderment and condescension. He quit the prized Asia head position for his wife... To move here? What a fool? Raahi thought to himself. At the same moment, however, Manisha's harsh words regarding his selfishness came rushing back to him and Mohit could glimpse the sadness they caused on his face. He was rather taken aback as he noticed this and when he spoke again, his voice was softer and more careful, "Yes, Raahi. What I did may sound insane, but who can be more important than family? How could I indulge my ambitions and be thrilled about it while my wife was at home worrying over her parents' health? It did not seem right to me. But then, I could be different." He paused and cautiously asked, "What about you, Raahi? Don't you have to negotiate changes keeping in mind your family's requirements?"

Raahi turned pale and replied brusquely, "Thankfully not! I made sure I don't get involved in this family trap. I am too fond of my independence. My life is meant for greater things and I keep focused on that. I have already changed jobs three times, you know. I am always on the look-out for better opportunities..." He gathered his thoughts before going on, "In fact, I left my last job only today. It was getting too much for me— they had me working obscene hours and the new board of directors is so stingy in their appreciation and bonuses. So I felt it was time for me to move on." As Raahi raised his voice towards the end, Mohit listened thoughtfully and silently observed the trace of fear and forced defiance on his face.

Clapping his hands together, he said, "Ah! So I seem to have met you on the right day. Now that you have all the time in the world, come, let us go home and celebrate our meeting..."

Raahi tried to brush away the invitation, but Mohit had made up his mind. Ultimately, Raahi was persuaded and he soon found himself comfortably seated on Mohit's terrace, enjoying the sound of the waves in the distance.

Mohit settled next to him and remarked, "We barely have a sea view, but at least we can hear it. I find it quite relaxing."

Raahi could only nod in agreement. The wooden flooring and the lush green plants all around him created a wonderfully soothing environment and he could feel his guard lowering. Afraid to let himself get too carried away, he looked suspiciously at Mohit and thought, Has he guessed what really happened? Why is he acting so friendly even though we have met after so many years? Is this his way of trying to get a good laugh at my expense? But, Raahi reminded himself, Mohit seemed too innocent to do such a thing. He was always a bit of a do-gooder—never a match for my shrewdness. If he does try to act smart, I will teach him a good lesson, he told himself.

Mohit, on the other hand, was too busy trying to be the perfect host to bother about anything else. "Are you sure you won't like some snacks with that? Dinner will take a while. Vandana will take at least another hour to reach and we always eat together. I trust you won't mind. Besides, you must meet her, she is always eager to meet my old friends."

"Don't you find that intrusive?" Raahi asked, slightly amused. "I would begin to find it irritable beyond a point."

Mohit knew he could expect such a comment from Raahi and was unfazed. "Perhaps, that's how you see it. I, for one, am grateful for such a loving companion. I feel it's only natural for her to take interest in the company I keep. After all, they say, we are the average of the five people we spend most time with, right"?

"Is that so?" Raahi sneered. "Then I guess that explains my strengths. I spend most of my time alone. Why mingle and bring down the quality to 'average'"?

Raahi was laughing, but Mohit was experienced enough to know that such expressions of bravado often hide behind them a dry, lonely existence. "Not in touch with many friends either, Raahi? Don't you meet any of the old guys anymore"?

Raahi shook his head negatively. "Not really, Mohit. Once in a blue moon, you know—if there is some important occasion, but not on a regular basis. I just don't have the time, to be honest. Today is an exception. Otherwise, I prefer to restrict myself to networking opportunities." This last bit Raahi said with some disdain, implying that Mohit was not a useful contact in any way. He meant to rub it into Mohit that he was not 'successful' enough compared to him, and evidently derived a kind of perverse pleasure in what was only the first of many such remarks to follow.

Mohit, for his part, remained unaffected by his friend's attempts to assert his superiority. He was not blind to what Raahi was doing, but chose to bear with it as he could sense that his friend was in some kind of distress, and even thought that he might need help, even if he didn't recognised it now.

As the evening progressed, Raahi began to grow increasingly unsure as to how to deal with this all accepting attitude from Mohit. Nothing he said seemed to provoke the man and he found it was equally difficult to intimidate or impress him with his exaggerated success stories. Eventually, he himself began to tire of his mask.

"It's getting late. Maybe I should leave. I am tired. It's a good thing I can sleep until late tomorrow," Raahi muttered.

"Sure, you do look tired and in need of a good night's sleep," Mohit replied gently. "In fact, if it is alright by you, why don't you stay over at my place tonight. We'll relive old memories together. It'll be good fun! And then tomorrow you can wake up all refreshed and start looking for your new job opportunity right away."

That was the last thing Raahi wanted to hear. He had had enough and angrily got to his feet exclaiming, "Look Mohit, I know what you are trying to do and I do not like it, ok. If you think I am in any way upset because I lost my job and my girlfriend today, then you are dead wrong and don't have a clue about me. I do not need anyone to patronize me and will come out of this even better than before on my own." That was it. Inadvertently, the truth had been spilt out. Mohit does not even have the grace to look surprised, he had already guessed, thought Raahi, furious with himself now. He immediately regretted his outburst.

Mohit's response was kind, but firm. "Calm down Raahi. There is no need to get upset. I am your friend and do not mean any harm. Please sit." A confused Raahi sat down to gather himself together.

"Look, I could tell in the park itself that you are badly struggling with a load of things. I also know that you don't like to take advice and how the unfair criticism you faced in college has played a huge role in making you what you are. Seeing you like this today, after so many years, I felt bad for you and wished to be there for you in whatever way I could. Please trust me and understand that I do not mean to put you down in any way..."

Raahi was overcome with conflicting emotions. His pride was hurt but a part of him was also amazed at this offer of support. For once, he was struggling for words. Nonetheless, his old habits got the better of him and he retorted dismissively, "Impressive lines, Mohit. But really, I don't think there is much you can do for me. Thank you for your words of wisdom, but I don't need either career or relationship advice from you! I am quite capable of finding another job when I feel like it. And as for women, they always chase a successful man so I have plenty to choose from. I think it would be better if I leave now!"

Mohit called out to him as he began to march off, but to no avail. Raahi pulled the door open but was surprised to find a beautiful woman standing there with a bunch of keys in her hand. She raised her eyebrow questioningly, observing his face all red with anger.

Mohit raced in just behind him and awkwardly introduced the two to each other, "Remember, I had mentioned Raahi from college? This is him."

Raahi was surprised that he had found mention in the couple's conversations, but only nodded curtly and said, "I was just leaving."

Vandana did not move. Her eyes connected with Mohit and they seemed to have a momentary silent exchange. She politely requested, "Do join us for dinner. You have met after so many years."

Raahi replied icily, "We have had more than enough time together. I have had my fill."

But Vandana only gave a warm, disarming smile, "Oh I can understand that! Mohit can be so talkative, isn't it? But we have only just met! Give me a chance to get to know you better. We can tell Mohit to stay quiet!"

Without really understanding why, Raahi felt his anger dissipating. These two people were being so kind and welcoming, could it be remotely possible that he was misjudging them? Too tired to continue his internal debate, and finding it difficult to refuse Vandana's polite invitation, he relented, "Oh well, as long as you can keep Mohit quiet..."

The evening continued on a more pleasant note as Vandana steered the conversation to lighter, more general matters. By the end of it, Raahi was feeling quite pleased and relaxed. While departing for his home, he remarked, "You know Mohit, as long as you mind your own business, you aren't such a pain. I do wonder how a beautiful, intelligent lady like this puts up with you."

Vandana spoke up playfully, "Oh, he has earned my affections, Raahi. It would be hard to find someone as considerate as him. You will learn, in time, to appreciate him as well. But for today, appreciating me is good enough!"

They all laughed and Raahi was on his way back, lost in thought. How differently Manisha would have responded, had she been in Vandana's shoes. She was far more impatient and curt and would never defend me...' But as he began to criticize her in his mind, he could not be blind to how he had seen Mohit genuinely make the effort to care for his wife as well. 'There is a genuine warmth between them. Undoubtedly, they work on making the other feel comfortable and loved. I wonder, was Manisha right in her complaints after all? He was afraid, and tried to shrug off the discomforting thought.

The next morning he received a text from Mohit, thanking him for a wonderful evening. He scratched his head, puzzled. What did it mean to thank someone for their company? Despite the reminder from Mohit and his good wishes for a successful job hunt, Raahi remained only languished in his house the entire day. Thoughts of the time he spent at his erstwhile office, rushed through his mind to take up his full attention and there seemed to be little he could do about it. For the first time in years, he acknowledged to himself that he was plagued with self-doubt.

Despite the false versions of different situations that he had been telling himself, the latter years had really not been a rosy period and he could vividly recall the number of times his boss had pulled him up. There had been poor judgment calls on his part and in solitude, he could admit to himself, however reluctantly, that many of his actions had arisen only from a desperation to avert crisis in the short term. His lack of detailed and timely efforts had often cost the company too much. Raahi sighed to himself. All this was more than he could digest. Could it actually be that my boss was right? No way. It was the company policies that were at fault. It was the ineffective and unfair system's fault, not mine. There was nothing for me to do but try and save myself on every occasion.

It was evening and Raahi decided to go the park again. Though he was feeling extremely lonely and frustrated, he could not bring himself to call Mohit again but secretly hoped he would find him in the park.

Fortunately, he did. "Oh good to see you, Raahi. I was hoping you would come by again. Come let's walk together. It always is a good way to clear the head, is it not?"

Raahi was much relieved. Whatever happened now, at least he was not alone.

This became a daily routine. They would walk for an hour or so and Mohit would begin the conversation with a concerned, *So how was your day?* He did not make a direct reference to how Raahi's search for a job was going. Even if Raahi did not answer at all at times, Mohit quietly understood, did not press him further and changed the topic.

Every few days, Raahi would join him and his wife for dinner and their warm hospitality was most comforting. They seemed to welcome him just as he was, whether he was in a silent, brooding mood, or a loud, talkative one. There was nothing to prove to them nor any need to do things to win their approval. Moreover, the way they interacted with each other and him, also made him introspect about his own attitude towards others in the past.

After a few weeks had gone by, Mohit decided to broach the subject seriously again. "Raahi, I know you prefer that I mind my own business, but as your friend, I do feel concerned for your welfare. I don't wish to impose myself on you in any way, but another friend's firm is looking for someone with your kind of profile. I feel you would be a good fit. If you like, I could put you in touch with him..."

This Raahi was not the same one Mohit had first met in the park several weeks ago. He had mellowed down considerably and, swallowing the pride that rose in his throat, reluctantly agreed to the proposal. The meeting went well and soon, Raahi could be seen working at his new job.

Though he attempted hard to be diligent and reminded himself repeatedly that he owed this job to Mohit's goodwill, within a month, his old demons came back to haunt him again and he was procrastinating working on a project urgently required for important research. This time, however, his growing nervousness and anxiety as the deadline loomed nearer was most palpable.

Mohit was alert enough to pick up such signals and could make out that his friend was on the verge of finding himself in a familiar situation again. One day during a conversation, he casually remarked, "You know Raahi, right from college, you have laughed at my careful preparation for the smallest tests or examinations. I know you say you like to work at the last minute, relying on the pressure of the moment to push you to put in the extra work and get more done in less time, but believe me, the sense of peace and accomplishment one gets from systematically planning and executing one's endeavours well in time is hard to describe. That way, I can assure you from personal experience, one never has any regrets, regardless of what the outcome turns out to be, because one knows one has put in one's best efforts."

He looked on as Raahi uncomfortably recalled all his moments of guilt and remorse at not having worked just a little harder on the project handed over to him and improved its quality. He knew very well that I may do a slack job but, despite that, he took the chance of recommending me. Even now, he is not telling me what to do, but telling me what his experience has been. What if there is some merit in what he says? I owe it to him to follow what he said sincerely.

Raahi actually lived up to the resolve he had made and acted on Mohit's advice. This time he managed to finish his assignment on the evening of the day before it was to be submitted. He was free and could relax now. It was a good feeling.

As he began to take a less arrogant and more diligent, reliable stance at work, his bosses were quick to appreciate him. Suddenly, he found that incentives and policies, similar to his last organisation, were actually now motivating and rewarding to him, because he had decided to improve his own inefficient ways of working. He was now keen to honestly deliver to his true capability and help his company progress. Raahi did not want Mohit to regret extending his help in any way. He was eager to do his friend proud.

A few weeks later, when he brought over his new girlfriend to meet Vandana and Mohit, he expressed his gratitude and regard for the couple out aloud as he introduced her to them, "Radha, come, meet my family. If you had met me a year back, I assure you, you would have run off in the opposite direction within a matter of days, never to return. If it were not for these two, I would have never realized what a narcissistic life of self-deception I had been leading for so many years. Their supportive company is what has gently nudged me back to becoming a more responsible and caring human being. I love them both from the bottom of my heart."

~

Gesturing to his wide-eyed students that he had finished, Areen went on to say, "Well go on now, think about this one and come back in an hour."

They did as they were told and when they returned to regroup, Ayushi's raised hand, asking for Areen's permission to speak up, met with a nod of acknowledgment from him.

"Friends like this are rare, aren't they? Most people generally tend to intrude into others' lives or try to force them to follow their advice even if it is not wanted. Raahi was rather fortunate," she said.

Drishti spoke up as well, "Yes, Areen. Vandana showed such tremendous patience. Why would anyone be so considerate? Raahi was quite a rude and arrogant person to start with. We usually tend to leave such people alone."

Areen responded, "Yes, you are both quite right. What Mohit and Vandana did may sound a little too good to be true, but trust me, such people do exist. I have learnt much from them myself. And one does not have to be very wealthy or intellectually brilliant to have a heart such as these people do. In fact, that can often be an impediment to identifying with someone else's pain; or, admitting to oneself that one is capable of making the same mistakes as someone else is, and therefore forgiving him and treating him compassionately. It is much easier to say that you cannot stand someone, than to care for him and help him change. Indeed, it is a sad reflection on the times we live in that sensitive people often hesitate to do 'too much good' even if they really sincerely want to, fearing that they either would appear artificial or manipulative or be taken advantage of, and force themselves to 'toughen up' to live by the standards of the world."

Arya was keen to speak next. "Areen, what you have just said, encourages me to share something which, though I was very proud of inwardly, I have always felt reluctant to speak of openly, afraid that it would seem too pompous and self-congratulatory. I think this would be a nice occasion for me to start."

"Go ahead, Arya. Sounds like you have something interesting to tell us," urged Areen.

"Well, I spend a lot of time online and, as odd as it may sound, one of my favourite pastimes is chatting with complete strangers. It started out as just a quirk, but, to my surprise, I made a few good friends along the way too. In fact, with all my experience, I often get a fairly accurate idea of what the personality of someone I am talking to online is, just by closely observing the information he has put up on his profile, how he reacts when asked personal questions, what kind of language he uses in general, and so on. Once you have had as many conversations as I have, this is not very difficult. Though I often got fooled in the beginning by people pretending to be who they were not, I can now say with some pride that many of my hunches have proven correct.

"Anyway, about three months back, I got a friend request from someone named Nishi. I accepted and we chatted for a while. She seemed to like the same music as I did and was even familiar with the rock bands I follow. As we continued our conversation though, the coincidences of our shared interests started to seem a bit too many.

"I could tell that there were things this girl was telling me, which just did not add up. She claimed to be from another city, but knew all the local hangout spots and college events in mine. A few unexpected questions I asked, took her by surprise and she made some well informed comments on local happenings. When I asked how she knew, she would say she heard about it from a friend or read about it on the internet or invent some other silly excuse. We did have several common friends, but what she said still did not strike me as true.

"For all these doubts about who she really was, somewhere, I did enjoy talking to this girl. There clearly were times when she was trying to pretend to be who she was not, and would feign interest in matters she actually was clueless about. But when she was 'herself,' she seemed quite a nice, sensitive person. Whatever it was, something between us had intuitively connected and I did not want to discontinue chatting with her. At times, we even had deep conversations on topics such as whether or not there is any point in being 'good', what does 'good' even mean, what it really means to be a friend, or what each of us really wanted the most in life..."

Arya paused for a moment to see all his bewildered companions staring at him, eyes wide open. They could not believe that the most restless boy of the lot, the one who complained the most about being in a place that was 'too peaceful' for his liking, whose world seemed to begin and end with the latest gadgets and video games, had this profound side to him too.

"What are you all so surprised at?" asked a slightly exasperated Arya, sensing that the minds of his peers had conveniently slotted him into the reductive category of 'spoilt, frivolous rich kid'. "Look, I know I come across as someone who would be one of the 'cool' guys at college, usually found hanging out with his friends at rock concerts and so on, and all that is true indeed, but that does not mean there is no depth to my personality. Even I think about such things and enjoy talking to someone who is willing to listen and respond. Who wouldn't?" He looked around in relief, as this time there were clear signs of understanding.

"Well, one day then, an incident took place which confirmed for me who she was, when in the midst of our conversation she suddenly blurted out, 'Oh, and what a wonderful answer you gave to that question in class today!' I was stunned to read that line and did not know what to write back. In the meantime, realizing what she had done, within moments Nishi logged out of chat. Having recovered from the shock of what I had just read, I asked the obvious questions, 'How do you know what I said? Are you in my class?' hoping she would respond, if not at that time, may be some time later that day.

"While waiting for her to say something, I tried to guess who she could be. No girl in my class was named, Nishi. Moreover, most boys and girls in class were my friends and why would they chat with me using a fake name. Maybe they would for a while, as a joke, but I had been chatting with Nishi now for almost a month and a half and that seemed too much for a friendly prank. Most importantly, I did share some intimate moments with her in this time, and they did not seem superficial or contrived on her part, so it was difficult for me to doubt her sincerity. Nonetheless, the fact that even after talking to her for so long I did not know we were in the same class, did shock me quite a bit.

"Needless to say, there was no reply from her the entire day. But I was not going to give up that easily. The next day at college, I made it a point to go up to each girl in my class, preferably when she was too busy doing something else to notice me approaching, and strike a conversation for at least five minutes, in the hope that I would be able to make out who I had been talking to online, from the way she reacted.

My idea worked, and eventually I knew that Nishi was actually Neelam, a girl from my accounts class. A quiet back bencher, she always kept very much to herself and when I went up to her to say a casual *Hello,* she was so petrified that she could barely lift her hand to reciprocate. Guilt was writ large on her face and after a few awkward moments, when she could figure out nothing else to do, she just ran away.

"As it is, she barely spoke to anyone and kept her earphones on all the time, almost as though she wished to ward people off from making conversation with her. It seemed strange to me how this same girl, Neelam, sounded so easygoing and friendly as Nishi.

"After class got over, I went up to her and said a polite *Hi,* and she reciprocated by shyly saying *Hi* back. But as I looked into her face–her eyes seemed to be giving me such a scared and pleading look that I was too surprised to say much more. In fact, the both of us just stood there looking at each other for about a minute. I knew she had realized that I had caught on to her and she did not want me to talk about it. She was desperately hoping that I would just understand and let her go. Intuitively, sensing the strong sense of fear about her, I thought it best to not pursue the matter further at the time and quietly walked away without attempting to strike a conversation."

"That night, I went looking for her online, but she did not show up. I spent much time wondering what her story was and why she did what she did.

"She came to class the next day, reaching just in time to get in. I glanced at her quite often, but she would not even look at me. After class, she ran off again. Of course, I know how it sounds. I have many people who would tell me that she had lied and she was afraid to be confronted. But I just could not believe it was that simple. I felt she needed a real friend for some reason. Someone who would accept this and not hold it against her... give her some time and space to figure it out. So I did what Mohit and Vandana did, acting as though there was nothing to comment about. I sent her a casual mail, asking her to contact me whenever she felt like. And I kept nodding to her in class.

"You won't believe the patience I showed. Routine messages online and nods of recognition in real life—I kept this up for almost three weeks, a very long time by my standards.

"Nishi never turned up again, but gradually, Neelam stopped running out of class. She began to give a shy smile and then actually began to exchange a few words. As she grew more comfortable, we actually began to strike up a proper friendship. Our conversations and easy connection there on, confirmed to me that this was the same Nishi. But that was one area that we both never touched upon.

"While it was all still a big mystery for me, I felt I was doing the right thing. Somewhere, my respecting her need to avoid that topic seemed to make her more trusting and somehow, immensely grateful.

"I told myself, it was ok. Perhaps she had been too shy to start with, so she put on this Nishi act. It is not a big deal and since she had dropped the story… we can let history be. We got along well and were really becoming good buddies.

"Finally, after almost four months, she finally rewarded my patience. We were out for a walk on the beach. As we strolled, she pointed out the waves washing away a sand castle.

"'See that?' she asked me. 'How the waves washed away a whole house in one swift movement? That is how it happened for me. My whole family just fell apart—overnight.'

"I looked at her in shock. She had never said much about her family. All I knew was that she was from Delhi and stayed in a girls' hostel here.

"'What happened?' I asked her carefully.

"'My father walked out on us last year. He left a note saying that he could no longer handle the restrictions and responsibilities of being a husband and father. He did not write anything more than that and… and just left! Can you imagine? How could someone do that to his own family?' She stopped walking and sat down on the sand.

"I sat down there with her, listening quietly, aghast at what she had been through."

"'It was as if my whole world had come crashing down. My mother seemed to have had all vitality sucked out of her, and went about life just like a zombie. She would work hard the whole day, come home and cry herself to sleep every night. I too, was completely torn apart, but was determined to get on with my life without being a victim. My mother was crying enough for us both. I knew I had to become mentally very strong now to deal with whatever had happened. There was still a part of me that wanted to make friends, wanted to believe that there were still people you could confide in. But I just did not know how to go about it—I did not know whom to speak to, I did not know what to think and I did not know if I could ever trust another human being again,' she said, shaking her head in dismay.

"'Almost despite myself then, I became extremely quiet and careful with people. Why set yourself up for pain, I thought. You believe in people and then they just run away one day, leaving you all by yourself. Better then to just play the game from a distance and not get involved. I thus adjudged it best to keep to myself and focus on my studies.

"'To gain some measure of illusory release in that chaotic time, I did one of the easiest things there was to do—create an online persona. This girl could be the person I did not have the courage to be anymore—carefree, happy-go-lucky, someone who could make friends as easily as I ran from them in real life. It did offer some kind of solace. And then, when I met you...' and she finally confessed what we had both known all along.

"'When I met you online as Nishi, I really began to enjoy our conversations. To be honest, you were the first person I could genuinely connect with after a really long time and we shared such great moments of friendship. But I was still too afraid to allow Neelam to replace Nishi. There was no way I could risk that kind of vulnerability. When you came and stood in front of me that day, I knew that you knew it was me you had been talking to, all this time, online. And if you had reacted judgmentally or even in a remotely hostile way, it would have left me shattered and I would have withdrawn further. I simply did not have the guts to be honest at that point. You have no clue how many times I have thanked you from the bottom of my heart for keeping quiet about this. Moreover, you went a step further and made the effort to actually befriend me in person.

Even though I seemed most unreceptive initially, I really needed someone to talk to but just found it too difficult to open up and express myself. If you had not been there for me, I don't know when I would have found the courage to allow myself to reach out to anyone in real life again. Who knows how much longer I would have probably continued with this strange, dual life?'

"Then, looking at me again, this time, straight in the eyes, she said with utmost sincerity, 'There is nothing like a true friend to get you through tough times. I am so grateful to you for your patience and understanding. I have started going for counselling, since the last couple of weeks. I was able to do so because you finally made me feel that it was safe and right to reach out for help. Thank you!' And with that she gave me a big hug. I cannot begin to tell you how happy and content I felt at the time. Right until today, Neelam is one of my best friends."

Arya ended his story with a satisfied smile, and Ayushi was the first one to voice her reaction. "Thank you for sharing that Arya," she said softly. "Who could have guessed so much was going on in Neelam's life? Knowing myself, I would have self-righteously given her a good lecture the moment I found out she had been deceiving me. But you were so much more sensitive and patient.

I have learnt something from you today and am proud to have you as a friend. Why did you never mention this before? Areen is so right. We don't talk about such things—and in the bargain we miss the basic human goodness that is right before us."

Similar compliments from the others made Arya grow red in the face.

Finally, Areen addressed them all in a sombre tone. "Thank you indeed, Arya. It is important to remember that we can often be blind to the challenges the other is going through. Sometimes, the best way forward is simply to be there for someone silently, not asking him for too much and yet being available for him should he need our help in any way. Just the way Arya was there for Neelam." Taking out a sun pendant from his Box, he said, "Here Ayushi, do accept this from me. It has always reminded me of how steadily the sun continues to shine its light and warmth for us, helping us find our own way. May it inspire you to be the same way for others."

Areen was now ready with his next story.

4

Anuj was angry. "Did you even think about why you want to have a child before you gave birth to me? Or the fact that everyone else has one was good enough reason for you? Where are you going? Answer me!" Declared the irate twenty-two-year old, as his father left the room banging the door, ending another one of their long, heated arguments.

His exasperated mother stood watching close by, in shock at this latest fit of rage. Angrily pointing her finger at him, she said, "Anuj! How can you speak like that to your father? Do you even realize what you are saying? Have you ever thought about how much he has done for you? Where do you even get these ideas! He got annoyed with you only because he is concerned about what you plan to do next, now that you have finished your graduation. And why shouldn't he be, you have postponed the decision for one whole year now even after so many discussions..."

Anuj stood his ground and was in no mood to spare anybody. "Oh really! It's that innocent, is it? Do you actually expect me to believe there is nothing else to it? If that is so, why is there a quarrel between two of the three of us in this house almost every alternate day? And if he is such a good human being, why do the two of you fight so often? When you have your arguments with him, you have some pretty nasty things to say. What rights then do any of you have to come and lecture me on how I should behave?"

Not wanting to listen to any more bitter remarks, Anuj's mother, too, left his room.

Though this particular altercation between father and son had indeed been quite extreme, minor incidents were a matter of daily life in the Gupta household. The situation had been very much the same ever since Anuj had entered his teens. A rather shy and obedient child, Anuj had turned into someone exactly the opposite as he had grown up. That his parents did not seem to get along very well between themselves made the situation even worse. Currently, in an utterly confused state of mind regarding which profession to take up for his future and the growing urgency he faced to settle into a career was getting little help from anywhere, least of all from home.

Terribly frustrated, with all these worries of past, present and future weighing on him heavily, Anuj felt a strong need to somehow take his mind off it all for a while. Picking up the newspaper lying next to him, he browsed through the advertisements section in the hope of finding some interesting activity or occupation. The announcement for a short, seven week creative writing course was what most caught his attention. How tough could this be? he thought. It will probably involve some casual reading and writing exercises. I'm fond of both these things so it should be a pleasant way to distract me from all this stress.

Contrary to Anuj's expectations, the course did demand a lot of work. But the classes were quite stimulating so he willingly put in the effort. He had not been the most expressive of people, so the opportunity to read authors who understood human feelings and emotions with such precision was such an eye-opener for him. It was rather fascinating to see how every word they wrote was chosen after careful deliberation, so as to convey exactly what they wanted. At times it almost seemed as if the writer had managed to pull out the words right from the back of Anuj's own head, clearly expressing a feeling that had been lying there, vague and dormant, since so very long. As the course progressed, Anuj grew increasingly interested in literature and writing, and would complete his assignments with much care and dedicated effort. His lecturer was quite impressed with him. She commended his writing several times and encouraged him to hone his skills even further. In the difficult time he was going through, her small, genuine gestures of appreciation offered much relief.

"Ok folks," the lecturer announced one day, "this is the course's penultimate week, and, suitably so, this week's exercise will be related to one of the most important things literature does. What it is, I will tell you all later. But first, what I want each of you to do is to write a letter to your parents, telling them exactly what you feel about them, whether it be love, hatred or indifference. Let loose completely and say all that you wish. Nobody but you is going to read the letter, so you do not have to worry about holding back."

As soon as he heard this, Anuj was overjoyed. He now had the chance to write about all the suffering he had gone through in his childhood and continued to go through until today. Writing about it would surely bring more clarity to him regarding the entire situation and hopefully serve as some kind of an emotional release—this was perhaps what the aim of the entire exercise was as well, he thought. Moreover, Ma'am had mentioned the terms 'hatred or indifference' herself, so she was obviously aware that, contrary to the popular stereotype, unconditional love is not always what children feel for their parents, and vice-versa. Without much ado then, Anuj began writing.

Dear Parents,

Sometimes I really wonder why the two of you got married to each other. You clearly have too many complaints about one another, and neither of you can seem to correct them to the other's satisfaction. Why then, even after you had got married did you just not go your separate ways? Even worse, why did you have to bring me into the picture? Father, you keep saying you had your failure in business to deal with and Mother, you say that your dreams of an ideal marriage were shattered when your temperament did not match your husband's and you had to deal with in-laws who were most unsupportive and prejudiced; but why did you still continue to bear with all of this for so many years? Moreover, what irritates me the most, is that whenever I confront you with any of this, instead of being even remotely honest about your relationship with each other or with me, you try to evade the issue altogether. Pretending that everything is fine does not make it so and I am not blind to the reality of the situation.

If you do not even begin to acknowledge that something is wrong, how can you ever hope to set it right? At least have the courage to admit the mistakes you made. If you think otherwise, I think you owe me an honest and believable explanation. I am tired of your typical response; when you do not have any answer to give me, you simply accuse *me* of being the one responsible for everything, for being the most insensitive, careless and irresponsible son in the world and leave the room. You neither hear my side of things, no matter how often I shout them out, nor do you bother to give me your side. How then do you expect me to respect you?

You claim that you have always wanted the best for me, that you did all you could to provide me with the best of everything. Perhaps that is what you would like to believe. But my own sense is that both of you just say things for the sake of saying them, without caring if your words really mean anything or not. You have in your head some ideal image of what a son should be, and you expect me to conform to it, all the time. Was I born only to live up to your expectations? The ambitions you failed to achieve in the prime of your lives, you wish to thrust on me to achieve for you. Can't you see how selfish and self centered you are being? That too at the cost of my life? Your capacity to deceive yourself and me by glossing this as a son's duty to his parents is remarkable. What do you think I am, some kind of a robot? Do you not realize that I have desires and wishes of my own?

Father, your constant comments of *I would never do things this way, You'll go wrong if you don't listen to me*, are most irritating. There have even been occasions when I have felt that you are actually trying to compete against me, and that too, in the smallest, most irrelevant of matters such as who can do a mathematical calculation faster or who is more well informed on current affairs. Too bad you think I make such a poor son; but to be honest you are not coming out as great as a parent either! And Mother, often when I have told you of my dreams, you have laughed them off insensitively. Instead of nurturing and supporting me, you have dismissed them (and me), claiming that you too had such idealistic views once upon a time, but they are destined to fail. What exactly do you achieve by behaving this way with your own son?

When I brought Avantika home recently to meet the two of you for the first time, all you had were cynical questions such as *Are you two really sure about each other, one reads of broken relationships so often these days. Does she know you have been sitting at home for over a year? Will she respect us?* etc. The list seemed to go on endlessly.

Moreover, the way you keep repeating how much you have done for me sometimes makes me suspect if you did all of it primarily because you expect me to do the same, or more, for you when I have the means to do so. Was I your retirement plan? If so, you need not worry. I will do my duty towards you financially when I start earning and return to you the debt that I owe. Emotionally, however, since I never received anything, I do not plan to return anything either. Even as I write this, a part of me feels that it really will not affect you even if you read it, owing to the remarkable expertise you have acquired over the years at playing the victim; so much so that you can spontaneously selectively interpret any situation to make yourself seem the most oppressed participant in it, without any regard for what actually happened. And the best part is that the both of you have been doing this with such supreme confidence that it has taken until now for me to figure it out. Nonetheless, it has been a relief just to put all this down on paper. Goodbye.

Your son,
Anuj

Anuj had managed to finish writing just in time for the class to end. He was quite satisfied with how his letter had turned out and, as he had expected, was feeling much lighter having unburdened himself through it. When it was time for everyone to leave, his lecturer went on to announce, "Alright, folks. I presume you all are done with your letters by now. I hope it was an interesting experience. However, do not think that this exercise was only about you giving vent to your repressed feelings and feeling better about yourselves. What I want you to do now is write a letter on your parents' behalf to yourself, expressing freely *their* feelings for you and *their* response to your letter. To do this, you need to first try and understand what is going on in their minds and hearts. After you go back home today, observe your parents carefully for the entire week and try to make as objective an assessment of their behavior as you can, trying to get an insight into their perspectives and feelings. Write their letter to you as sincerely as you have written your letter to them. Keep in mind that not only literary texts, but people's personalities too have contexts as to where they come from. Several layers of meaning can be found not only in the passages of Shakespeare's plays, but also in the inadequately phrased expressions and the tiniest involuntary twitching of the facial expressions that are part of everyday conversations. Learn to recognize the intricacies of motivation not only in the fictional characters of novels and plays, but in human beings as well. We are complex creatures and communicate at many different levels. Sense the energy in the room, the weight in what is unsaid… pay attention to everything. Good luck and see you next week."

This turn of events was especially surprising for Anuj. Why would Ma'am want us to do this second exercise? he thought to himself. I am quite sure I have judged my parents objectively enough over all these years to know how they think. What difference is writing a letter on their behalf going to make? Anyway, now that we have been given the assignment, I will try to make it as well as I can.

Thus, he followed his lecturer's instructions sincerely and, when he sat down to write the letter at the end of the week, came to some surprising conclusions.

Dear Anuj,

When we first read your letter, we were speechless and did not know how to respond. Nevertheless, we have discussed between ourselves what we wanted to say to you and this is your father writing back on behalf of both your mother and myself. As your parents, we feel it is our duty to try to have you understand that we are not your enemies, but are 'on your side', as it were. It seems that, despite our best efforts we have not been able to communicate clearly with you, son. Looking at ourselves objectively, we can see that we do not make it easy for you. We feel something, but say something else, so that at the end, only a close look at *what we finally do* can give you any understanding of the kind of people we are and what our attitude is towards you. It is a rather muddled way of going about things, we can admit that. But you have to see that this is not intentional, it is just how we have come to be over the years. You must bear in mind, son, that we are not as educated as you. You have studied in the best of colleges and even had the privilege of being taught by private tutors, both luxuries not available to us. In fact, given the prevalent belief of her times, your mother's own parents, though they sent her to college, encouraged her not to concentrate too much on her education and focus more on the household, because that is what was supposed to matter more for her as a woman. A college degree would look good on her resume when people came to ask for her hand in marriage and that was its only importance. As for myself, I was reasonably good at my studies, but, generally speaking, men of our times were never really encouraged to pay attention to or express their feelings, so I lag behind in that department a great degree. Moreover, while you had the privilege of growing up in an upper-middle class house in the well developed city of Delhi, neither of us did. I was brought up in the small town of Varanasi, your mother in Bareilly and both of us had very had little exposure to the world beyond that.

When I was a student, I did not even know how to speak fluent English and felt inferior to classmates whose insults at my 'lower-middle class behavior' I had to grow accustomed to. Perhaps my need to prove my superiority, wherever and whenever I can, comes from there... You do not get over such scars easily, Anuj. They tend to become a part of you.

You ask why we got married or chose to remain married if we had so many problems with each other. Yours is a different generation and trends have changed considerably, but your mother was twenty one when she got married and I was twenty six. That is how things happened in our times. Marriage was considered a compulsory part of life, something that had to be done and that too at the 'right' age. Compared to today, you cannot even imagine the kind of place it occupied in everyone's imagination then, especially in the small, conservative societies that we belonged to. Many years from now when you look back at your younger days, you will surely find things you did, which you assumed just had to be done and seemed a given, things about which your own child's generation, will think differently.

You are right in saying that your mother and I have had our fair share of troubles. Our relationship began to turn sour soon after our marriage when I could not give her time as my business had failed and I was forced to start from scratch. In your letter you have mentioned my failure in business in the passing, but I do not think you have fully understood the significance of that event in my life. My best friend, someone I regarded as part of my own family, cheated me, son. Do you realize what that means? Your mother, for her part, just could not take what had happened. Her childhood had been rather oppressed due to tyrannical parents who gave none of their children any freedom at all, constantly keeping check on the smallest of their activities. Like most girls of her time, she had been led to believe that marriage worse the most momentous occasion of a woman's life, the beginning of some kind of a golden age, where all her troubles would automatically be taken care of. When this did not happen, she was as emotionally scarred as I was, and we could be of little help to each other. Neither of us had anybody else to confide in, as well.

You ask if we even thought about what it means to have a child before we had you. Well, to be honest, we did not. There is no denying that, just like marriage, having children too was considered a necessary and natural progression of life then. Not wanting a child would have been an unthinkable anomaly, at least not one either your mother or I were capable of. Your generation is a questioning generation. Which is good in a way. But not all traditional thought is without value. No one, all by himself can figure everything out. When you feel inadequate and alone as we did, it was a relief to take things on trust, to rely on age old ways of living. They seemed to work well enough for everyone else, why would they be difficult for us? We too, wanted a happy family and thought that a child would help light up our lives with joy.

You did, believe me, you did. But we also learnt along the way something that we had naively not anticipated—that bringing up a child involves great responsibility. Somehow, no one had described all the challenges that came along with it. We understood this only in hindsight, through experience. If at times we impose the image of an ideal son on you, you can take consolation in the fact that we too, are constantly battling with ourselves to live up to our own idea of ideal parents. We feel we have failed, every time we have one of our clashes with you. Your anger makes us feel completely inadequate. No one taught us how to be parents, and we are struggling along, sometimes actually pretending to be far surer of ourselves than we really feel. If nothing else, we start blaming each other for the way things have turned out.

Though none of us had the courage to discuss it seriously, the option of divorce had crossed both our minds several times. But once you came into the picture, the unstated understanding between the two of us was that we must stay together for your sake. We do not say this to fill you with gratitude towards us, but just to answer some of the questions you had raised.

But to be honest, we do not think it has all been bad. I know it may seem like that to you, because the fights always tend to stand out in one's mind. I used to think like that earlier too. But I later realized that just because many things at home had settled into a kind of routine, a kind of given, I had completely neglected noticing them and took them for granted. So, when I came back from work late, and still had hot, well-cooked food right before me, I would forget to note that it was your mother and nobody else who had to warm it for me again so that it tastes better. Had a friend done the same thing, how grateful I would have been towards him and thought him to be such a nice person. Similarly, if I found the beds laid neatly, everything kept in its proper place and the bathrooms bright and sparkling everyday, none of it happened automatically. Your mother had to make the effort to do it so that I could conveniently get on with my office work, and she did so even when we had the worst of fights. Think about it and I am sure even you will find that there are many occasions when we feel glad to have the togetherness and security of family holding us intact. These are usually forgotten and it is mostly the negative aspects that remain highlighted in all our minds.

Also, I am sorry if we came across as too cynical about Avantika. It may not seem so, but we were just concerned because we know how much effort and compromise it takes to make a marriage last. Our generation was told that that was the way it worked, but it still has been no easy task. So, naturally now, when it comes to you, we worry. You youngsters are more used to either having it your way or giving it up. How then will you negotiate the many challenges, especially those of differences in perspective, that a marriage brings up unless the both of you are determined to make it work? This worry is what expressed itself, as the barrage of questions we assailed you with, but perhaps you are right, there were better ways of saying what we wanted to.

Here, in the comfort of our present home, you do not really know how it feels when you do not have the money to buy something you really want for yourself. Your mother and I have been through such a phase and, believe me, it is not easy to bear. Yes, we may be both selfish as you say, but there is also great truth in the fact that we wanted to keep you as away from such a fate as was possible and tried to give you whatever comforts we could. This is also one of the reasons behind our insistence that you choose a lucrative career. As your parents, we do not wish to see you suffer the pains and insecurities we have dealt with for much of our life. What if you take as long to settle financially as I did? How will Avantika react? Will she be able to make the extreme compromises that your mother had to? Perhaps you will only understand this when you have a child of your own. And yes, this may sound like one of those standard clichéd answers you detest, but really son, some clichés come about for a reason.

There have been times in the past, and even today, when I am racked with self-doubt as to why I have done what I have done in life, what I did right and where I went wrong. But as hard as I have tried to search, I have never been able to find final, definitive answers to these doubts. I don't know, perhaps I am asking these questions too late in life. So, for my own peace of mind, I have more or less decided it is best to carry on without thinking too much. The same holds true for your mother as well. If you can find greater clarity than us regarding these questions, good for you, son. We avoid the disturbing questions about our lives you confront us with, because frankly, beyond a point, we really do not have any answers to give either to ourselves or you, and that makes it too painful to talk about such matters... And even if we do find the explanations, I wonder if you would really be able to understand the complexity of it all.

After reading your letter, we are afraid that you will dismiss this as one more of our attempts at providing justifications for our behavior. But son, the sad truth of it that we have come to realize as we put this reply together is that yes, we are fearful people. We were afraid of our parents, our society, our peers and now we are afraid of you. We have simply kept moving along, trying to do the best we could and more often than not, we have failed in the eyes of others and ourselves. We have also clearly disappointed you no end. But whether we are able to convince you of it or not, the one consolation we do have, is that there is one place where we are very sure of ourselves and that is in our love and concern for you. If you can ever see that, our lives would have been well lived, at least in our opinion.

We may never fully understand each other Anuj. Perhaps, that never really happens between parent and child. But if this exchange of letters can help us be a little kinder towards each other, a little more accepting—it would be a welcome relief to us as well.

Sincerely,
Your parents

"Hmm... I can make out from the buzz in class that writing the second letter has been quite an interesting experience for most of you," said the lecturer as the last class of the creative writing course commenced. "I felt the same way the day I tried it myself the first time. I hope your introduction to literature in these seven weeks has contributed in some way to a more nuanced understanding of life. You see, this is one of the most important things good literature does, it makes us care for the human being, it helps us understand him from his own point of view. This last session of ours will just comprise brief, private exchanges between myself and each of you individually, so we can discuss your thoughts on this last exercise. I will meet you all one by one now. Let's get started." The writing of this second letter was cathartic for all those who had attempted it sensitively.

Anuj sat brooding and silent and waited for his turn to come. The week had not been easy for him and he had put up great resistance in trying to look at his parents beyond all his complaints against them. When he went up to Ma'am to talk about his experience, he admitted to her candidly, "I feel rather ashamed of the letter I initially wrote now, Ma'am. It just seems too trivial and blinkered. I am still to fully absorb all that the second letter taught me, but as I was writing it, I felt frightened, perplexed, humbled and saddened all at once. Also, it was fascinating to see my parents treat me most of the time, is completely forgotten when I am hurt by their scathing words. Why is it so hard for them to demonstrate care more gently? Do they always have to resort to criticism and correction? When they realize they are wrong, why can they not change?" he said irritably, falling silent after that.

The lecturer nodded thoughtfully, "You are right, Anuj. I am happy that you have been honest enough to try and see your relationship with your parents objectively. It is difficult for everyone to reflect upon their behavior, admit where they are wrong and implement change. Tell me, are you not struggling with the same thing now, when you can see that some of your habitual ways of seeing things have turned out wrong? Did you begin remedying your flaws immediately, the moment you recognized them? That is not true, is it?. Your parents are also the same, Anuj. Things take time. People have conflicting motives, thoughts and behaviors They often say things they do not mean or do things they had claimed they never would. Too often they do not express what they want to, and hide what they should not. Most of us are struggling to learn our way towards a balanced and integrous being. That is life. Literature offers us the gift of being able to spell out the many facets, the diverse factors that go into our making and helps prevent us from remaining trapped in our own singular, uni-dimensional perspective. I have read your assignments and it is clear you have the makings of a writer. Being open to the many points of view that co-exist in reality and comprise its beauty will only help you come up with new, enriching insights and expand your readers' worldviews as well. I wish you very good luck for the future. It really was a pleasure to have interacted with you during this course. Do keep in touch."

~

This story had been particularly hard-hitting, especially as it dealt with the parent-child relationship often seen as so sacred in society. Areen had anticipated the stunned silence of his young friends, who did not know where to look or what to think. Different aspects of the story had hit home with each of them, but this was not something they had ever discussed openly. Whatever be the truths of their respective households, in public one was always expected to extol the virtues of the family and demonstrate an unquestioning obedience and respect for elders. This time, the one hour break was much needed.

When they returned, Aditi was brave enough to start by confessing, "That was rather shocking, Areen. We are not used to hearing such stories about parents and children. How different it was from what we usually see on television or in films. Family relationships are presented so ideally there and we, too, watch what is shown with such longing. But I guess if we were to be honest with ourselves, we would all admit that it is not as simple as such portrayals would have us believe. Your story, though quite disturbing, seemed much closer to reality. Anuj seemed to have quite a volatile relationship with his parents, but surely many of us, to different degrees, could identify with it. I strongly felt, however, that the most valuable part of the story was the way Anuj learns to see things from another person's perspective. Initially, when Anuj wrote his own account of his childhood and his relationship with his parents, I was quite taken in by it and my sympathies lay with him. However, as he began to inhabit his parents' shoes and see things from their point of view, I began to do so along with him and it just put things in such a different light. It was so much more difficult to take sides then. Or rather, one didn't really want to take sides after that. I'm certainly going to try this letter writing technique when my relationships go wrong. In fact, I already have someone in mind to address—my elder sister, with whom I quarrel bitterly almost every day."

Areen was glad that Aditi had set things in motion with such an honest response. He had thought it would need much more coaxing to get honest feedback on this story given the nature of its content. "Is there anyone else who would like to say something?" he asked.

Soumya raised her hand and was allowed to speak. "I am quite disturbed by the story, Areen. But it has provoked me to think, that is for sure, and I have some questions. Areen, doesn't this story suggest that human beings are mere puppets of their circumstances? Couldn't Anuj's parents have done anything at all to alter their lives for the better? Couldn't Anuj have done anything at all to not go through such a troubled childhood and teenage? Does this mean that, fundamentally, we have no choice or responsibility in the actions we perform? Is that not a terribly disturbing conclusion? Surely, there must be something one could do to assert oneself over the circumstances one finds oneself in?"

Areen responded, "Interesting question, Soumya. Surely, people's mindsets, beliefs, views of the world and even everyday decisions are influenced by their circumstances and conditioning. And it would also obviously be too simplistic to think that one can rationalize it all and arrive at the exact reasons for why a certain person acted a certain way at a certain point in time. But, despite this complex framework, yes, I believe that finally, we do have a choice in the way we act. We can choose to exercise restraint or let ourselves succumb. Nonetheless, alongside the awareness that we can choose to act differently, we should also keep in mind that we are only human; and that it is human to make mistakes, to choose poorly in the heat of the moment, or to give in to fears and distractions.

Personally, my own guiding principle is to be as conscious as possible in my choices and to encourage others to do the same. The more we are aware of our own 'governing framework' and our present state of mind and emotions, the more likely we are to make evolved choices. Otherwise, we run on autopilot, having little idea of why we are doing what we are doing in life. What I am doing here with all of you is itself a part of this attempt to be and help others be more conscious. To make them care for their fellow human beings, to make them aware that each act has some consequence or the other in the larger world; that it makes a difference to the lives of other people, to make them ask themselves if they really want to spend the short time life gives them, hurting people or helping them, spreading love and joy or anger and hatred. That is one of the main things which keeps me going."

There was a reflective silence as they all pondered over what Areen had just said. Aditi still looked perplexed so Areen asked her what was on her mind.

"I do see your point of view Areen. But I wonder if this whole emphasis on understanding where others come from and sympathizing with them without imposing any judgment or correction can go too far? It does make us feel rather noble and evolved and all of that, but really, if someone needs to be shown his erroneous ways, is not the better thing to do simply to point out what he has done wrong and tell him to mind his behavior? There are times when the way certain people act is just too disturbing and being a passive observer to it is also wrong!"

"Thank you for the question, Aditi. I am glad you raised that point. Empathy and compassion must not be confused with encouraging or allowing any form of harmful behavior. It means addressing the problem from its roots, and how will you do that if you do not understand the source of the wrongdoer's pain; the source which lies in the lack of proper nurturing that the mind and heart of such a man has received, and which we have been fortunate enough to have. By all means, do whatever is required to prevent wrongdoing; after all, if someone comes to rob your house with a gun in his hand, it would be foolish to 'appeal compassionately to the goodness of his heart' —that may well result in you losing all you have. Nonetheless, in all this, do not forget your own link, however small, to that person as human being. Being compassionate to another does not exclude taking care of yourself. It means to respond in a manner that keeps in mind thoughtfulness to all concerned. One can both empathize with someone, and understand why he did what he did, but at the same time also point out that what he did was wrong. People often confuse ideas of 'love' and 'acceptance' with being a doormat. That is not what it means. Change is only possible when you see the situation as it is. Only then can the right action arise from a deeper wisdom."

Soumya spoke quietly, "That is such an important lesson to remember, Areen. I think we often forget to see things from another's points of view. We are so busy defending what we think is right, that we fail to see that others may think themselves to be right too, in their own way."

"Indeed, Soumya. A lot of the issues in the world today are because of this simple oversight on our parts. There are diverse perspectives in the world and we need to respect the fact that they are valid from their own frames of reference. Only then can meaningful dialogue and peaceful coexistence truly begin.

Here, this small metallic soap is my gift for you—to remember that we need to clear our own vision of its clouds and not blinkered by our own perspective alone before we can see the whole picture for what it is. We need to come from a space of love, not fear, nor judgment. This will allow us to understand and respect difference, and find the most appropriate way forward.

"Alright friends, it has been a long evening and I am sure you can all do with a good night's sleep now. That would be a fine way to assimilate the experiences of the day." said Areen. There were a few protests, but Areen politely dismissed them. "I am delighted to see how much you are enjoying our little game. But too much of a good thing is not good. We will continue tomorrow night, I give you my word. Rest tonight and awake afresh for a new tomorrow. It is the first day of the rest of your life. Goodnight."

∽

The friends could barely contain their curiosity through the day. They were eager to hear more stories. Having rushed through their dinner, the entire group huddled around the Box. The flickering light of the lamp seemed to amplify the anticipation on their faces.

5

Reshma shouted out in exasperation, as she threw aside the book she was reading. "Nothing is working out! Why can't I just stop thinking about this?"

She had been trying hard to distract her troubled mind since the last several hours. But, everything she tried only seemed to make her more aware of the very thoughts she was avoiding. She called up her friend Aman and began to complain. No sooner did he say, "Hello", than she started off. "I just can't take it anymore, Aman! I went for a walk, but the children playing happily on the lawns just reminded me of how alone I have been since you left the city. I don't have any other friends in this new place and I cannot even remember the last time I laughed! I tried to listen to some songs on the radio, but all they played were those mushy, sentimental Hindi film love songs with not a grain of truth in them. The television is even more depressing. There is news of corruption and scams only! Even watching my favourite comedy film, something which always helps lift my spirits, has not worked. Worse than that, even chocolates have failed! All this has made me so angry, I cannot even begin to..."

"Calm down, calm down, Reshma. At least tell me what happened?" asked Aman, afraid to think what lay further if even after saying so much, Reshma felt she had not even begun.

"Aman, I feel like the most unhappy and lonely person in the world right now. I just want to get away from it all... The last of my entrances got over yesterday, and I have little doubt that I will not make it to any of the good management schools I want to study in. Try as I might, I just cannot fathom how to crack these entrances. I really think I am not made for them. When I try to speak to my father, all he can say is that I should try to figure out where I went wrong and do better the next time. If I do not qualify anywhere, I will have to remain stuck in my incredibly monotonous translation job for one more year. Believe me, if I had enough finances to support myself, I would just..."

"Oh come on, Reshma, do not behave like a child. It is not so bad. So, you could not clear an exam and are bored with your job. It is not the end of the world, is it? Your father's advice seems pretty valid to me. What do you mean when you say 'you are not made for these entrances'? Instead of discussing the issue with others, sit down with yourself and apply your mind to pin down where you are going wrong, correct it and improve. Outside help will be pointless if you yourself take no trouble to resolve the problem. Everything does not happen instantly, does it? Anyway, I just remembered... Didn't you have a dinner date today with that handsome guy you had told me about? Is that not something to look forward to, to brighten up the day?" Aman reminded her, trying to cheer her up.

"Oh thanks for bringing that up! He cancelled today, after a week of waiting. He says he has been asked to work overtime today. Can you believe it? I don't. Maybe he stayed back just to cancel on me!" she ended bitterly.

Aman gave up. "Reshma, take it easy. There is no point talking to you when you are like this. Maybe we can speak later in the evening?"

"Fine. I should not have called you in the first place!" she snapped curtly and ended the call.

She stomped over to her study table to pick up her journal and jot down her thoughts. Frowning at the long line of books before her, she grumbled to herself, "Whatever possessed me that I bought all these self help and spirituality books? I should have known better. After years of remaining stuck in a miserable pattern, alternating between being depressed about life and somehow barely managing to cope with it, why haven't I just given up? What is the point of carrying on?" Randomly opening a blank page she began writing furiously...

> Even as I write this, I am angry with myself for continuing to use this method of journaling in the illusion that it will help me vent my emotions, think more clearly and feel better. The problem is that I have gotten so used to doing all these things for a change of mood now, that I fall back on them mechanically and the exercise has lost its value. After all, where has it really got me? I still have these thoroughly wretched days when I wish I did not even have to get out of bed. Oh God, where

is all this leading? You feel better for a while and the world comes crashing down again, what is one to do with this life?'

She wrote on for a while and after about a dozen pages of complaining, her hand started to hurt due to its tight hold on the pen. Taking a deep breath, she got up from her chair to look out of the window. The horrible day was coming to a close. Sighing in relief, Reshma pushed her chair away from her desk and stepped into the balcony. Leaning against the railing, she looked down and saw Vinit watering the plants.

A hard-working and pleasant young boy, barely sixteen years of age, Vinit was effectively the entire society's man friday. His father was supposed to be in charge of the general maintenance of the building, including the upkeep of the gardens, lawns and playing areas. However, it was Vinit who turned up in his place on most days. Reshma would be happy to chat with him occasionally as she strolled in the gardens. They shared a relationship of affection and Vinit looked up to Reshma as a kind of elder sister. Along with this work in the day, he regularly attended night school and was an eager learner. Reshma was only too glad to help him with his studies and answer all the questions he often had for her.

Feeling the weight of Reshma's gaze, Vinit looked up distractedly. Reshma was stunned to see his face distraught, with eyes all red and swollen. She had never seen Vinit like this.

Suddenly forgetting her own troubles, Reshma rushed downstairs moving with a new energy. As she approached Vinit, he looked away, pretending to be too busy with his work. This was in sharp contrast to his usual enthusiasm on seeing her. "Hello Vinit," she called out, worried for his well-being.

He turned back reluctantly and greeted her, "Namaste, *Didi*. How are you?"

Looking at him with concern, Reshma asked directly, "What is the matter with you? Have you been crying?"

Crestfallen as he was, Vinit tried to put up a brave front and deny it. Finally, he shamefacedly confessed, "I am sorry, *Didi*. I know men are not supposed to cry. And you are always telling me to be hopeful for a better tomorrow. But..." He looked down quietly as, much to his own deep embarrassment, he burst into tears.

Quite taken aback, Reshma instinctively tried to comfort her little friend. "First of all, Vinit, it is nonsense that men are not supposed to cry. Crying or expressing any of one's emotions is good for all human beings. But do tell me what has happened? I have never seen you in such a terrible state."

Vinit stood staring at the ground, his anger at having allowed himself to cry growing by the minute. Finally, he managed to get a few words out, "*Didi*... Father has forced me to leave school..."

"What?" Cried out Reshma, visibly shocked. "How could he do that? You are such a bright and hard-working young boy. I have taught you myself and can vouch for that. Did you not do well in your examinations this time?"

"I was among the highest scorers *Didi*, but Father says he just cannot afford to educate me anymore. If that were actually the case, I would not have felt so bad, but I know he is blatantly lying. Drunkard that he is, he wastes most of the money that me and my sister and mother earn, on alcohol and gambling. When we try to resist, he beats us mercilessly. I cannot stand him, I wish he would just die."

Prompted to tell Vinit not to speak of his father in such a way, Reshma held herself back, realizing that this was not the time for such a moralistic stance. Feeling for the agony she saw in Vinit's eyes at the time, she attempted to comfort him in whatever way she could. "Hmm… Now I understand why he is not here for work so often and sends you instead. Why do the three of you need to stay with such a person, Vinit? If you are the earning members of the family, why tolerate such behavior from him? Why don't you just walk out on him?"

"My sister and I are ready to do that any day. But we just cannot understand our mother's attitude in this matter. Even after suffering all my father's abuse and having bitter fights with him almost every day, she still insists on how 'after all, he is her husband and our father, and we must stay together as a family'. It is only out of regard for Mother that my sister and I still stay in that house, else we would have left long ago.

"In fact, Mother is not entirely unsupportive of the decision of me leaving school. She too feels we need to save more money for the dowry my sister's marriage requires. I don't know… but sometimes I think she is right in saying so. What will I really be able to achieve even if I continue my studies in any case? At the most, they will last for another year or two and a tenth standard pass qualification is the most I can hope to achieve; and at end of the day, that is not going to get me a far better job than the one I am currently engaged in. I cannot think only for myself. Having an unmarried sister in the house would bring far more shame on all of us, especially on her, than my not completing my education. She is already twenty five years old and it is getting late. What face will she, or even Mother and I, show in society if we cannot get her married…They are both already so embarrassed and upset by the delay. You don't know what it is like in our community, *Didi*."

Brushing his sleeves against his cheeks, wet with tears, he carried on, "I am tired now, *Didi*. I am totally fed up! Sometimes I really think it is pointless to carry on living a life like mine. Why don't I just give up? This constant effort is only prolonging my misery. I know you will be very disappointed to hear me say this, but I cannot take it anymore. I am sorry I wasted your time with all my questions. You too, should stop wasting more time on me *Didi*, nothing will come of it. I am destined to remain trapped like this."

Vinit's last lines were very similar to what Reshma had just been saying to herself alone in her room. But when she compared her reasons for saying them to his, she felt herself go numb. Though she outwardly maintained her composure, what she had just heard from Vinit had left her extremely ashamed and with very little to say. After a few moments of awkward silence, she resolved that she could not let Vinit go away just like that and forced herself to speak up. "Don't worry, Vinit. Don't lose hope like this. Some door or the other will surely open for you…" she said, though these words did not sound convincing even to herself.

Vinit's tears had dried and he was beginning to regain control of himself. "I am extremely sorry for breaking down in front of you this way, *Didi*. Please do not tell anyone what I told you. It was just that today, I felt I had had enough. Coming here fresh from a beating my father gave me, I was feeling very helpless.

When you came and asked me so gently how I was feeling, I could not control my tears. Talking to you has made me feel better. Thank you." His genuine gratitude to Reshma for lending a patient and understanding ear to his woes was evident from the expression on his face. He went on,"I will leave now. The building elevator has been out of order since the last two days and I must finish repairing it as soon as possible."

As soon as he left, Reshma felt the strong wave of sympathy that she had kept under control until then, overwhelm her fully. Her eyes grew misty as she reflected on how this poor boy, whom she had been treating with such benevolent superiority until now, who looked up to *her* for guidance and advice, had so much going on in his heart. At such a young age, he had faced conditions so harsh that they were difficult for Reshma to even imagine. Her own problems seemed trivial and insignificant in comparison. She felt shallow and exceedingly foolish. How completely wrapped up she had been in her own minor difficulties to have had the audacity to see herself as 'depressed'.

What was even more remarkable about young Vinit was that one could hardly ever see any sign of his troubles on his face. Reshma recalled his conspicuously cheerful and affable mood while watering the plants and doing everyday chores that the maintenance of the building required. From the care with which he carried out each of these tasks, it seemed that he found enjoyment in these little moments themselves. Once, for example, Reshma had noticed him talking to one of the flowers as if to a friend, encouraging it to grow quickly. She sighed heavily and thought to herself, All this time I have been doing the teaching, whereas there was so much to learn from this boy.

Having arrived at this realization, Reshma rushed to the elevator Vinit was busy repairing. As soon as she got there, she called out to him. "Vinit, come here and listen well to me." When the boy came close to her wondering what the urgency in her voice meant, Reshma smiled at him warmly. "What are the fees you need to pay to continue with your education, Vinit?"

Filled with hope at the promise the question seemed to hold, the boy replied, "It is one thousand two hundred rupees for four months, *Didi*..."

"Whatever it is Vinit, I earn enough and will pay for your school education right up to class twelve. I will pay the fees directly at school, so that your father cannot interfere in the matter or take the money away from you. I am aware of some scholarships after that which can help you get through college. But you must promise me that you will never lose hope again, as you did today, and will work as hard as you can. Believe me, it will not go waste. It will take you further than you think right now. The important thing, Vinit, is to not stop trying."

These last lines, as Reshma knew very well, applied not only to Vinit, but to her as well.

The young boy, in turn, was overwhelmed with emotion and tears trickled down his cheeks. This time, however, they were born of gratitude, relief and renewed hope.

~

Areen's story had ended, and it was time for everyone to leave for the routine one hour break. But Swapnil was most enthused and, almost despite himself, blurted out, "You won't believe it Areen, but I have a great personal story to tell which resonates quite strongly with this one. I cannot wait to share it with the others so may we please start right away? This is just the first story of the day and I am sure we could all do without our interval at least this time?"

Areen laughed a little and looked around him to see that Swapnil's proposition clearly had support from all his friends. Encouraged by their bright and eager faces, he granted their request. "Alright folks, we will not take our scheduled break this time. Go on, Swapnil. Let's hear your story."

"Your story, Areen, reminded me of my cousin, Apeksha's humbling experience with caring and giving. Apeksha had always prided herself immensely on her integrity. Both her parents are distinguished scholars and she has had the good fortune of being brought up in a household where an eclectic collection of books and films were always at her disposal. Her family also had a string of visitors who would gather for many an intellectual discussion or debate on various topics and Apeksha would often sit in, listening to these from an early age. She is so well read and knowledgeable that whenever all us cousins would meet at family gatherings or otherwise, we could not help feeling as if she was our superior, rather than someone our own age.

"She, however, was not arrogant and neither did she like to flaunt her extensive knowledge. But, even topics that came naturally to her in conversation, the rest of us barely had a clue of. I understood this and would often laugh about it with her openly, so we got along fine. But there was always a kind of distance between her and the others, who found it difficult to connect with her and she with them. Even some of our elder relatives faced similar problems with her, and the end result of it all was that she was labelled as a haughty and snobbish girl by most of the family. To them, it appeared that she was deliberately trying to put them down.

"Apeksha, in turn, felt deeply hurt when she sensed that despite having no ill intent in mind, she was being judged so harshly. Incensed by the constant suggestions to apologize to those she had supposedly hurt or been disrespectful towards, she preferred to stay away from the family and spend time alone, or in the select company of a handful of friends with whom she shared similar interests.

"Having completed her three years' undergraduate course in philosophy, Apeksha decided to take a break from her studies and teach children English at one of the local schools. When she joined, however, she was in for quite a shock. Her new environment was replete with rumour-mongering, gossip and cut-throat competition, on a scale she had never seen before. Her knowledge, integrity and commitment to work, instead of being welcomed as an asset to the school, only served to alienate her from her peers and especially those in positions of authority, who were threatened by it. For her part, convinced that she was doing the right thing, Apeksha stood by her values despite the criticism she faced.

"However, things kept getting more difficult at work. Now the subject of much malicious slander herself, Apeksha grew increasingly quiet and began to have a constant air of sadness about her. Her warm, gentle nature seemed to have taken a beating and, worried for her, I invited her to my place one day to ask how she was doing. Things were clearly not going well and even the smallest of Apeksha's gestures of kindness and good natured generosity towards both her colleagues as well as her students were misconstrued as having some ulterior motive or the other. Her description of the atmosphere of distrust and suspicion in a school staffroom of all places, left me rather shocked."

Swapnil gritted his teeth, "The poor girl was not getting an iota of the gratitude or respect she deserved. She was just innocently being herself. I guess it was probably too hard for those people to believe that people who are genuinely interested in their work and believe in goodness for goodness' sake still exist."

"That's terrible," said Sheetal. "Why didn't she just quit? Or talk to the headmistress? How could she let them get away with this?"

Swapnil went on, "She did not want to quit her job for such reasons. And neither did she want to descend to their level. A situation then arose, however, which forced her to speak to the headmistress, Madam Rustomji, the only person she truly respected in that school, about all that was going on. It turned out that Apeksha's colleagues had tried to poison the headmistress against her. Too experienced to fall for such tricks and well aware of Apeksha's dedication and sincerity to the school's progress, the headmistress called Apeksha to her office to ask her if she was facing any difficulty in the school. Apeksha heaved a sigh of relief as she had finally found someone she could trust and gave vent to all that was inside her regarding the happenings in the school. Her anger at the fact that people who had studied to become teachers and were supposed to act as role models for the students were indulging in such pettiness was unpalpable.

Madam Rustomji's reaction, however, was not quite what Apeksha had expected. Instead of being as infuriated as Apeksha was about the situation, she calmly told her that she was already aware of what the staffroom atmosphere was like. She then advised Apeksha to be patient and considerate with the way her colleagues behaved with her, explaining that such actions were mainly a result of troubled hearts and insecure minds. Apeksha was reluctant to accept the headmistress' views. She thought this as her way of trying to make peace between her and her colleagues, so that they could coexist without causing too much trouble to the functioning of the school. So she heard Madam out, without really agreeing with any of it, reciprocating the courtesy that the headmistress had demonstrated by listening to her side of things. Nothing really changed.

"After another few days, I met Apeksha again and this time, she looked even more agitated. On asking her what was wrong, she told me how she had been put in charge of school supplies for the primary section, but many of the items she purchased every week were found missing. It started with minor things, such as a few colour boxes and tennis balls, but as the days passed, the list kept growing. This came as no surprise as all the items were being kept in a makeshift shed in a part of the school that was undergoing renovation, access to which was easy for anyone.

"Apeksha was very upset and had a strong suspicion that the construction workers' children were stealing these items. None of the other teachers bothered to help her. They told her it was her responsibility to keep stock and she would have to face the consequences of her incompetence. Apeksha was struggling to find a solution to the situation.

"One day, just after a new collection of toys had been brought in, Apeksha decided to stay back after school and keep a close eye on the shed. As she had suspected, some of the construction workers' children came out to play in the area with a football that she herself had purchased for the school. These children had stolen the ball from the room and seemed intent on doing the same with the new toys that had come in. So, she went up and confronted them."

Arya could not help interrupting, "That was not a very smart thing to do!"

"No it wasn't," agreed Swapnil, "Even though they were children, far from being scared of Apeksha, they were rude and aggressive. They denied any knowledge of the thefts Apeksha accused them of, claimed that they had bought the ball themselves and told her to mind her own business."

"That could not have been easy for her to take," remarked Sheetal.

"No, it certainly wasn't. She was unaccustomed to dealing with such rough behavior and thought it best to report the matter to the headmistress, hoping she could suggest an appropriate way to deal with the situation.

"Madam Rustomji heard Apeksha out carefully as she informed her of the child-thieves and expressed her bewilderment at the fact that she had even seen the ends of a few *beedis* and empty alcohol bottles strewn around where these children lived. She shuddered as she spoke of this. 'I could not believe it, Madam. I thought I was wrong and that this could not have been the work of these children. May be it was their parents. But yesterday, when I saw the way they behaved, I would not be very surprised if they indulged in smoking and drinking too. These children have grown far older than others their age, Madam. They are very different.'

"'They have to be, Apeksha,' replied Madam Rustomji after a brief pause. 'They have no choice but to fend for themselves, sometimes even against their own parents. They have to manage in whatever way they can. However, we should not lose sight of the fact that despite that, they are children. Like any other student in our school, what they need is love and caring.'

"Apeksha could not contain her indignant surprise at the headmistress's attitude. 'What does that mean, Ma'am? Are you saying we won't be taking any strict action against them for what they have done? Isn't the whole point of running an educational institution, to inculcate values and appropriate behavior in the next generation? These children are heading down the wrong path. If we do not teach them that there are consequences to such behavior, who can imagine where they will end up and what other crimes they may commit. Even if it is their parents or environment that has led to this, they *must* be stopped now. Our passiveness would contribute not only to their degeneration, but also be responsible for the harm they cause others in society. Madam, I think that it is important we punish them and teach them a lesson; set an example in some way. The first thing I think we should do is to get them to return our toys and forbid them from using these grounds so that they do not end up negatively influencing our school's children as well. We need to be firm so that none of this is encouraged and they come back to some sense of decent standards.'

"Apeksha had been unable to restrain herself and was sure she would be reprimanded for her outburst, but Madam Rustomji was calm as ever in her response. 'No, no. We need not do any such thing. These children do not have lives, Apeksha. We can let the toys be for now. If not our students, other children are playing with them. You are right about not ignoring any of this, but shunning them away completely is not the answer. Instead of treating only the symptoms of the problem, we need to treat the roots of the problem. We need to address their needs for constructive activity, for hope and for some self-respect. We need to think of how we can bring some joy into their lives.'

"'Simplistic lectures on morality are not going to help. Since we allow them on the grounds anyway, I would suggest we start a small class for them after school? Not formal teaching, but simple, basic things such as respecting others, maintaining hygiene, why smoking and alcohol will get them nowhere, perhaps do all this through or along with some song and dance, or art and games? Just to let them know, in some small way, that they matter too.

"'I feel it will help if we could simply connect to them as human beings, without being overtly righteous or anything... that would be good for a start. But who will do this, Apeksha? I do not have the funds for it. It will have to be voluntary. Would you like to take this on?' Apeksha hesitated. She was sceptical if Madam's compassionate approach would work with these children and feared it would be taken advantage of, just as her gentleness had been misunderstood and trampled over by her own colleagues in school. Sensing her apprehensions, Madam smiled and said, 'I have a suggestion. Since we both came up with this idea, we should both give it a fair trial. What if we were to try this out together for a month? We can see how it goes and then decide how to take it further.'

"Out of respect for Madam Rustomji, Apeksha finally agreed to the proposal. In any case, she too was keen that *something* be done. Initially, both of them found it difficult to befriend these children and have them attend their 'fun-hour' sessions. The little ones were rather wary of this sudden generosity to start with. They were not accustomed to gentle behavior of any sort and looked at it with suspicion. When they did begin coming for class, there were incidents of abusive language and fights and disagreements all the time. It was completely different from the school teaching that Apeksha was used to. But it was evident within the first few days itself that the children were also quite talented and when they enjoyed what they were doing, they kept to themselves, engrossed in their work.

"After one month, when Madam and Apeksha sat down to take stock of how far they had progressed, they found that though the thefts had not stopped, they had been significantly reduced. And only one window pane had been broken since they started. Not once had they lectured on theft, graffiti or damage to property. They just kept their attention focussed on being genuinely friendly with the kids. One more teacher joined them as children from a nearby slum had also started coming. In addition, one of the school parents offered to sponsor a nutritious evening snack to supplement the biscuits they had been arranging for, from their own pocket. Greatly encouraged by these positive results, Apeksha readily agreed to continue to manage the program by herself.

"Gradually, more changes became evident. One day they found all the scribbles on the shed wall washed off. *Beedis* and bottles were finally conspicuous by their absence from the ground. Even the window pane was miraculously replaced one night. Slowly but surely, even the stolen material began coming back—one day a broken bat, another day three tennis balls, and so on. No child confessed and no teacher questioned. Things just seemed to return to their proper places on their own. What she saw, humbled Apeksha considerably. When the same children who had once rudely rebuffed her came up to her and thanked her for teaching them so well, she felt deeply gratified and wanted to do so much more for them. Madam Rustomji was right. All these children needed was the right guidance and they were capable of doing as well as anybody else.

"The ripple effects of Apeksha's experience with the workers' children spread to the staffroom as well and what she had learnt there helped her broaden her horizons when it came to dealing with her colleagues. The other teachers could not help but notice and respond to the change in her. With her more down to earth attitude and willingness to cooperate, there were now much fewer occasions of disagreement. She even took a few of them out for coffee once, and this helped break the ice further.

They remarked, 'You know, we thought you were such an uppity, self righteous snob! But we were quite wrong it seems. You are quite a nice person."

Apeksha could only respond similarly, 'Oh that's alright. Let bygones be bygones. I also had a completely different opinion about you. I guess we should learn to know each other better, before we make up our minds about people isn't it?'

"It has been a couple of years since all this happened. Apeksha is now in charge of the centre post school hours. Children from the nearby slum have voluntarily assumed responsibility for its cleanliness and safety. Working mothers can now leave their young toddlers there as some basic crèche-like facilities have been put in place. The older children now receive support to return to municipal schools or obtain vocational training. The whole project has taken a life of its own and Apeksha is as happy as can be. Many of the other staff members also support her work and she now has some good friends among them. They have all learnt to help each other out.

"My dear cousin is now the first one to remind me that any advantages we have been lucky enough to have are only wasted if not passed down to others. Our gifts are not meant to feed our pride and should not be used as reasons to look down on others as incapable of doing what we can, but instead to serve those who have not been as fortunate. She is clearly inspired by Madam Rustomji and I can see why. She has learnt much from her indeed.

Swapnil ended proudly, "Amazing isn't it? How much she changed? And the teachers and children as well? Just one person's persistent effort can set off such wide spreading ripples of goodness."

"Absolutely," smiled Areen. "That was a wonderful story to share, Swapnil. I must add it to my Box's repertoire. It may inspire many more to go out there and do whatever little they can. Who knows how far it may go, isn't it?"

"Great story Swapnil, thanks! Makes me wonder what small acts of kindness I can commit to?" said Aditi thoughtfully.

"That is a useful thought. Why don't we all take a few minutes to make our own resolutions?" proposed Ayushi, as lost in tracing the borders of the sun pendant Areen had given her.

Areen welcomed the idea. He did make a cautionary observation though, "Make sure you commit to something you are sincere about, no matter how small it is. It is not necessary that you share this with anyone, but declaring it out aloud does help. It makes us feel accountable to each other. The point here is not to impress anyone, but to do whatever comes genuinely from one's heart."

They all nodded in understanding. There was nobody's approval to gain. But there would always be one's own conscience to answer to.

As they finished, Areen handed over a thin metallic bracelet made of simple, interlocking chains to Aditi, "There. May this always remind you of the interdependence of us all."

6

Areen waited for a while after the last story until everyone had settled comfortably again, and then began, "Well, as I had said at the beginning, this is a space where we all participate, speaking and listening from the heart. Since we have been talking of learning to think beyond established boundaries so much, let us try and practice what we preach in the format of this game itself. Instead of me narrating the next story, I would like to know if any of you wish to take the floor instead."

His brief glance around the room caught Malhar's eyes and, sensing that the young boy was anxious to say something, gave him the cue to speak up.

Summoning up some courage, Malhar said, "Well, in light of some of the issues we have been discussing, Areen, I wanted to talk about something that has been bothering me very much since quite a long time. I might as well open up about it here in front of my friends and you and hope for some clarity. Who knows when I may get such a chance again..."

"Of course, please go ahead Malhar," Areen said gently.

"I am actually struggling with my ideas about role models right now. You know, we look up to our mentors and tend to elevate them in our minds. They are such an inspiration. And when we are emotionally attached to them, the bond means so much more..." Malhar stopped, sighing heavily for a moment before continuing.

"My maternal uncle was Dr. Sankara and he belonged to a small village near Allahabad. Ever since he was a child, his life's ambition was to enter the medical profession. He knew what it was like to live in poverty; to live a life in which meagre basic amenities were considered luxuries, and where, if one fell ill, one did not even have a competent enough doctor close by for help. He had lost his father to a heart attack right before his eyes for the very same reason—neither did the doctor arrive in time, nor was the equipment he had at his disposal, adequate. Before they could take him elsewhere for treatment, his father was gone and there was nothing he could do about it. That very day, Uncle vowed to dedicate his life to serving the people as a doctor himself, and to improve the medical conditions in his own village, as well as in as many others as he could. He laboured day and night to make the best use of the education the village school could provide him. Fortunately, he had some city relatives to help him where the school lacked. Subsequently, he successfully cleared the entrance exam for one of the top medical colleges in India and his relatives continued to lend him funds to complete his education. Bit by bit, he was inching closer to his dream and had no intention of stopping midway.

"I know all this in such detail because I have spent long hours listening to him tell his stories. My father was barely around when

I was growing up, so Uncle was the one I turned to most often, for guidance and company. He was my friend, philosopher and guide, all rolled into one. Anyone who met him could see that he was this confident, passionate individual who was determined to change the world. Even during his years in college he was full of idealistic ideas of how people could be healed and lives could be transformed because of modern medicine. His idealism was infectious, and I was only too eager to catch on to it.

"His performance as a student in college was excellent and the best of hospitals were keen to take him on as an intern. Equally enthusiastic to join them, he chose to start off with a big private hospital in Delhi. He felt that there was much to learn here in terms of the latest advancements in medical research and efficient ways to run a hospital. He knew he needed such experience before he could move on to setting up his own hospitals in rural areas. But right from the beginning, he swore to himself that he would not be dazzled by the glitz and glamour that the larger private hospitals reeked of. He worked with great dedication, impressing most of his seniors with his innovative ideas to change the established system for the better.

After Uncle's internship was over, he stuck to his original resolve and left this grand hospital to start his own practice from scratch. This was no easy task. There were innumerable challenges and his insistence on honest and scrupulous practice made it quite difficult for him to survive in a setup rife with corruption. He made it a point to resist the crafty kindness of pharmaceutical companies who wanted him to promote their products over those of others, refused to prescribe more medicines to his patients than were really needed and charged them only as much was actually due. Uncle carried on like this for five whole years, confident that one day he would achieve what he had set out for and that too, on his own terms.

"One particular incident, however, left him so deeply scarred that it changed his entire way of life. A very senior surgeon from a 'reputed' private hospital (famous among the general public but notorious within the medical community for its complete ethical bankruptcy) had invited Uncle to be the chief guest at an inaugural function. Not wanting to associate himself with such people, Uncle politely but firmly declined. This irked the surgeon so much that he left no stone unturned and used all his power and influence to have my uncle's clinic shut down. Can you believe it? Such pettiness for as small an issue as declining an invitation! Uncle was shattered. He had never felt so helpless in his entire life and that too, for no fault of his own. He knew he was right, but just could not do anything to defend himself. Those he was up against just had too much power and clout. It was only the discerning advice of a few experienced lawyer friends and a great amount of luck that finally managed to get Uncle out of the situation. After this disaster was over, it was evident how disillusioned he had become with the entire system. Despite all these years of dedicated effort, if all it took for his clinic to be shut down was a few phone calls from some deluded, power-hungry maniac, then what had he really achieved?

The feelings of being hurt and insulted gradually led to a sense of despair at the unfairness of it all. Though he never admitted it outright, one could see that his confidence had begun failing when he saw less competent doctors, people who had started out as his juniors racing ahead of him in terms of fame and material success. One had his own hospital, another owned a BMW, a third was building a palatial new home; in contrast, his own burden of loans was only growing. His investment in a small building for his first hospital had brought about tremendous pressure and every call from a financier would embarrass him no end. His self respect was fast deteriorating. Isolated and alone, he began to feel that his modest background had made nothing but an unrealistic dreamer out of him."

Malhar sighed and went on, "He confessed that, though he resisted it at first, all these factors and especially his burgeoning debts compelled him to begin toeing the line and somewhere, he began to compromise his values. In order to get more patients, the hospital needed referrals from other doctors, which meant he had to reciprocate likewise. It started with minor things such as this, but before he knew what was happening, it had grown out of his control. Unnecessary diagnoses, tests, hospitalizations and eventually even avoidable surgeries became the norm. There were sponsored international trips and high stakes in the form of incentives from various pharmaceutical companies which asked for major covering-up and fudging of research data in return. On the one hand, his practice and the hospital itself were a roaring 'success' and he could expand his reach to several other locations just as he had originally envisaged; on the other, this was not the kind of service he had set out to provide and he was no longer the same person. He had sold his soul. The price for success was a heavy one to pay.

"When people in the family spoke about the devious means he was resorting to, I could not believe it and told myself I was misunderstanding what was going on. But when too many stories began to emerge, my confidence in my mentor began to give away. My mother too, grew increasingly upset and suggested that I stay away from Uncle to avoid his bad influence. I even tried asking him to explain, but he was curt and said it was not so easy to live by the principles one would like to; that one has to compromise to cope with the harsh realities of everyday life. I kept trying to argue with him and eventually, he snapped at me in anger and told me to mind my own business..."

Malhar fell quiet, shaking his head in sadness, but Areen gently prompted him to go on.

"His high stress occupation and lifestyle of indulgent excess were eating away at his health and family life. Strange, isn't it? A cardiologist completely neglecting matters of his own health and heart. He succumbed to a heart attack two months ago. His death gave a lot of patients the courage to express their outrage against him and more stories of malpractice emerged nineteen to the dozen. Apparently, he had been able to suppress all this via his money and power while he was alive."

His eyes all red, Malhar looked at Areen and said, "I have not been able to get over his loss yet, Areen. Not his death, as much as his loss—I lost my revered mentor well before he died. I feel so sickened by it all. I just cannot understand what happened. What happened, Areen? How could someone whose beginning was so inspirational, end up turning into the very thing he had started out opposing in the first place? For all his ideals when he started his journey, in his last years Uncle was no less irresponsible than the doctor who arrived late to attend to his father's heart attack, and no less a power-hungry maniac than the senior surgeon who had shut down his clinic for most shallow reasons. What made him turn into such a ruthless, unethical, self-seeking wreck? Was he never the person I thought him to be? Had he been fooling all of us and himself for so long?"

Areen could see how deeply pained Malhar was and responded carefully, "Malhar, I can understand how torn apart you have been feeling. Life often throws at us these heart wrenching challenges and we need to take stock of such situations with courage and objectivity. Tell me, if you can only for a few minutes set aside all that happened with your uncle in his later years and allow yourself to reconnect with the energy and the feelings that you had when your Uncle would spend time with you initially, do you really feel that he was being fake or fooling you?"

Malhar quietly relived his memories for a few moments and then said, "Well... no. It does not feel like that at all. He really seemed to want to change the world for the better. But then... If he was so genuine, how did he change into such a... a monster? How can it be the same person"?

"Malhar, you must understand that simply categorizing people as either 'good' or 'bad', 'black' or 'white' is too myopic a way to look at them. That is not how people are in real life. Each human being is a rather complex individual with not just one but many sides to him, many 'selves within him', as it were, all of which, together, constitute who he is, and we must learn to look at him that way. This holds true for all of us, not just anyone in particular. So, if you really love your girlfriend and think she is a wonderful person, there can still be aspects of her that you just cannot stand and there is nothing wrong with that. Similarly, if someone is extremely arrogant, hypocritical and manipulative, there may still be aspects of him that are admirable—such as his sharp intelligence, and again, it is absolutely alright if one feels admiration for this particular quality of this otherwise deplorable personality. One should not feel guilty about these things.

"With regard to your uncle's case specifically, you need to realize, Malhar, that if we generally see someone as a 'good' person because of the deeds he has done, that does not mean that there is some 'core', 'essential' 'goodness' deep within him which is permanently going to make him act that way. He can still choose to do wrong at any point of time he wants. Who is to stop him from doing so? Sure, it would be unlikely that a person who has done what is right for much of his life suddenly acts in the opposite manner, but the point is that he can if he wants or has to. Each one of us is capable of good or bad choices and behavior and so was your uncle. From what you told us of him, it seemed quite clear that the humiliating experience with the surgeon affected him so deeply that he just did not want to carry on with his idealism anymore. You must acknowledge to yourself that he did make that choice, Malhar. That was the way he decided to go. Moreover, another thing I think it is important to say to you is that it is alright to respect someone profoundly, but it is perhaps unreasonable to turn him into an unrealistic idol and place the entire burden of flawless, unfailing goodness on his shoulders. Such elevation is more than likely to lead to disappointment and even his smallest human errors will have one declaring that your idol has developed feet of clay. Similarly, the people one impulsively classifies as incorrigibly 'evil,' as it were, if one looks at them closely, one may find they are not so bad after all. We tend to exaggerate things to one extreme or the other, while the truth usually lies somewhere in between.

"Living up to the values that we look up to is, indeed, rarely easy. It takes a long while to start seeing that what seems extremely difficult in the immediate, actually brings us far more lasting peace and joy in the long run, than tempting and easy short-term compromises. We are all on a learning journey here, and what we need to do is learn from the mistakes we ourselves make and those we observe others make. Nonethless, Malhar, stories such as that of your uncle should not lead you to conclude that all idealism in itself is futile and each idealist's fate is to end up as cynical and defeated. You do not *have* to do what he did. The values he believed in, when he started, were not worthless and you made no mistake by imbibing them. Just as you learnt admirable things from your uncle in his earlier days, there are surely some things that you can find to learn from the latter half of his life as well?"

"From the latter half?" Malhar asked, very surprised at the suggestion.

"Yes, most definitely," said Areen. "You can learn to avoid the pitfalls he, for whatever reason, could not or did not. You can learn what not to do to avoid a fate such as his. Very importantly, you could learn that it is not enough to have ideals, but that a deeper strength and conviction need to be built in order to sustain them when we enter the 'real' world."

Malhar nodded in agreement, finding much sense in what Areen was saying.

"I can assure you, such strength of spirit is much needed to face the many obstacles that cross one's path when one is dedicated to a cause. One other thing that strikes me about your uncle's story is that he was too alone in all his endeavours. Certainly, there are times when one has to be courageous enough to stand up independently for what one believes in, but one must keep in mind that there are always others in the world whose ideas about improving society are similar to one's own; and being in touch with such like-minded groups of people is most helpful and necessary to stay on track. It gives us the much needed assurance that we are not all alone in fighting for our cause but have the genuine support of friends who are as committed as we are. Perhaps another area where he erred was that, because of his firm belief that his ideas were actually quite brilliant and meant to achieve ends for the betterment of everyone and not just a few, he did not anticipate that there would still be people who would try to oppose him for reasons of their own. That was naïve on his part. Moreover, 'being true to oneself and false to no man' is a desirable ideal to follow, there is no doubt about that. But one must also be frank enough to admit that, realistically speaking, there are often situations one encounters in life, where an unsophisticated understanding and application of it could severely backfire and have dire consequences, and a more practical approach would be required instead.

Anyway, to come back to your uncle, Malhar, I have not been saying all this to demean him or negate his achievements in any way. But it is important to recognize that each one of us has his limitations, and can be blissfully unaware of them even if they stare him right in the face. Your uncle's remarkable focus and determination to set out to accomplish what he intended to, is evident just from the little we have heard of him. It was just that he eventually channelized these qualities in the wrong direction."

Areen had said enough and all his young students had been listening with rapt attention, especially Malhar. The furrow in his brow as well as the look of awe on his face signalled that though a lot was still going through his mind, he had found some clarity as to how to think about his uncle's seemingly incomprehensible behavior.

"Has this conversation helped you feel a little better, Malhar?" Areen asked with concern.

Malhar nodded his head emphatically and said, "Yes it has, Areen. Thank you. I have made a mental note of all that you have said, and will reflect on it again in private so I can grasp it better. Though I will not be able to articulate it if you ask me right now, I know that I have understood something."

"That is good, Malhar. But do work on finding the words for what you feel. It really is a beautiful process and will help you understand yourself and others much better. It may seem difficult in the beginning, but once you get going you will begin to recognize its value, you will want to do it willingly. Reading good books will be of great help in this, I can assure you. So, what about the others... Does anyone want to say anything?"

Sheetal raised her hand and said, "I am reminded of my Mathematics professor in college, Areen. Most of the students do not like him because he seems too arrogant and never seems to agree with our answers, always finding something or the other lacking in them. I, however, have always looked up to him because, to my mind, though he is strict and often too blunt in pointing out where we have gone wrong, he seems to want to do so not out of the desire to insult us or prove his superiority, but to help us improve as students. At the risk of being unpopular in our eyes, he sees it as his duty to tell us where we have done well and where we need to grow, because nobody else probably will. Moreover, such is his great love for his subject, that he even takes six hour classes with only two breaks in between without either us or him getting the least bit tired. His enthusiasm when he teaches is such a joy to watch that we begin to appreciate the beauty of the subject along with him. I would always find myself short of words when I would want to defend him against my classmates' prejudiced opinions because I would not want to bring in even one remotely negative word when speaking about him. However, what you have just told us, Areen, has helped untie a few knots in my head, and I have realized that it is fine to say that yes, Sir can be nasty and irritable at times, but by no means should that mean that we ignore the other wonderful and admirable qualities he has. He is not interested in being a saint and I should not try to make him one.

On the other hand, a History professor we have is just the opposite. He hardly ever takes class and can be perpetually found gossiping with his colleagues in the staffroom. Consequently, the syllabus is never finished on time and at the end of the year, he just rushes through some of the basic questions to pretend to make an effort, which is actually of no value and from which no one learns anything. Nonetheless, because he speaks to the students as if they were his friends and praises them to get on their good books, he is most popular in our class."

Areen nodded thoughtfully, "Yes, that often happens, Sheetal. That something is popular does not necessarily mean it is of the best quality. So, you need to be careful and think for yourself. How much of good and bad you imbibe from others is eventually up to you. While it is extremely important to trust, it is also important to be vigilant as the best of us can go wrong, often without our knowing it. Right Malhar?"

Malhar nodded in agreement and gratefully accepted the toy tea strainer that Areen handed to him from his Box, "A reminder, Malhar, to selectively filter what you choose to take in. Take the good things and leave the rest."

~

An astonished Ayushi asked, "What is this?" She saw Areen take out another strange object from his 'Box of Tales.'

"Its a small piece of driftwood," answered Areen.

Ayushi turned the curved and twisted piece round in her hand and remarked, "It looks polished, as though a craftsman had tried to give it some shape."

Areen responded knowingly, "If you are willing and ready, you will see what life wants to show you. Much like this piece of floating wood that was polished by the ebb and flow of tides, we are all shaped by the trials and gifts of life that leave us much stronger and wiser than we were before. Sunil's story has something to say about this. He was kind enough to share it with the participants of our last camp. Perhaps all of you will find it of value too."

7

Sunil was exhausted and drenched in sweat. It had taken great effort to complete the three kilometre run. Once he got his breath back, he turned to his coach, Amit, and said, "Not bad, right? It's been well over three weeks now since I missed a day."

Amit smiled in approval and replied, "Yes, you have been amazingly persistent. I did not expect you to make such remarkable progress so quickly. Hats off to your grit, Sunil. You have braved a great amount of pain to get this far."

Sunil gave a satisfied nod. "Yes. The doctors are in for a surprise. They never thought I would regain this level of physical fitness. But thanks to you and your training, the accident is slowly becoming a distant memory," he said as shook his head sadly for a moment, the mere mention of the accident unsettling him a bit.

Amit seemed to sense what was going through his mind and replied, "That really was a terrible crash, Sunil. Do not make light of it. Though you are sticking to your plan with such determination, allow yourself to be human. Losing your best friend and being told soon after that your chances as a football player are practically nil, are both huge shocks to deal with. I am aware that you had known Anil for over ten years, and that you had nurtured the dream of making it to the national football team ever since you were a toddler. To have all that taken away from you in such quick succession would be an unbearable setback for the strongest of people. How do you expect to let go of it all without any remnants of pain?"

Stirred by the concerns his coach raised, a defiant Sunil answered, "Just the way I proved everyone wrong about my injury. No doubt it will take a lot of work and I still have a long way to go before I can make it back into the college team. But at least I have some chance now as compared to earlier, when the best of doctors had said there was no hope at all. Similarly, if I focus hard enough, I will forget that the accident ever happened and not let it weigh me down." Grumbling in frustration and repressed anger, he further said, "Anil was a fool. I had warned him so many times not to drink and drive, but did he listen? No! Instead, he insisted that he could handle it. And look how he paid for it... Look how I am paying for his stupidity! I will not let this ruin my life. I will not let it haunt me. I will move on and with such force that this entire episode will become irrelevant to my life, as if it had never happened. Everything will be the way it was before. Just let me return to the game. Once I am back on that field, no one will remember any of this, not even me."

Amit did not know what to say to this declaration. Sunil's determination was admirable but Amit's experience in the sport told him that he was being impractical and unrealistic. At the same time, he did not want to dissuade Sunil from his most cherished goal and hoped that his experience would be proven wrong. Nonetheless, he went on to offer whatever advice he could in the given circumstances. "Sunil, as your coach and trainer, I feel it is important for you to deal with the emotional trauma you went through. You cannot simply wish it away. Physical fitness is one thing, but a balanced mind is important too. How do you expect to perform to the best of your abilities, when you carry all this anger and frustration inside? I cannot force you, but I will not stop reminding you that you must find a way to release all this emotional baggage."

Sunil stood up abruptly and, wincing at the throbbing pain in his right leg, replied, "Amit, thanks a lot, but do leave this one to me. I have no time for this 'emotional self development' jargon. My main goal, right now, is to return to the team by pushing my body to its peak again. I have a plan and I intend to stick to it. I don't need anything but good exercise, physiotherapy and nutrition. You are helping me take care of all that and the results are showing. Nothing can stop me."

Little did Sunil know, how his confidence was misplaced.

Despite back-breaking effort, the degree of fitness he finally managed to achieve did not match the standard that the team required. As the team's coach, it was, again, Amit, who had to explain the situation to him, this time more plainly than earlier. "I know how difficult this is for you Sunil. But you need to accept the situation. You are a great sportsman, but you can no longer play this game. Let it go now. Don't torture yourself like this. I am sorry. I really am. I would have loved to have you back in the team. But it is not possible." Saying this, he walked away, feeling sorry for his friend.

Sunil sat by himself on a bench close to the football ground all day, alone and dejected. He was too upset to go anywhere else. While some of his old team mates awkwardly avoided him, the others had nothing to offer but words of consolation.

Practice session being over by the evening, Amit walked up to Sunil to try and cheer him up, "Don't let this get you down, Sunil. What you have achieved is commendable. Who knows, perhaps something better is waiting for you. Even after the accident you are healthier than most people. What more could one ask for? Perhaps all this will lead to something better that you are not being able to envision right now..."

No sooner were these words said, than Sunil's eyes flashed with anger. His jaw clenched and he snapped at Anil, "I ask for a lot more! How on earth do you expect me to accept that this is going to lead me somewhere better? A lifelong dream down the drain... after all the effort I put in, slogging so hard, shedding blood, sweat and tears. This is what I thought I was born for—to be a football player. The one thing I wanted the most has been snatched away from me and you tell me that this will lead to something better? How much more do I have to pay for the idiocy of letting a drunk friend drive me home? Forget it, Amit. You cannot possibly understand what I am going through right now. Perhaps this is as far as you could help me. Thanks and goodbye."

Amit tried to calm him down. He felt bad for Sunil, but also felt compelled to speak the truth. "I know you are upset right now, Sunil. But as your well-wisher, I have to help you face reality. You can see that your football career is over. Now you can cry about it, get depressed and let it eat into your future, or you can see what more you can do with your life. There is always much left to learn in life, my friend. You have already learnt so much from sports, and surely there will be things to learn from this accident and the suffering it has caused you—don't let it make you bitter like this..."

Sunil could no longer contain his growing fury anymore and lashed out, "I think it is best you stop talking now! I respect all that you have done for me. But you clearly don't get it." Stepping closer to Amit he whispered acidly, "I wish the accident had killed me. It did not make me stronger. It has left me a cripple, as far as the game is concerned. There is nothing left for me to live for. Consolatory speeches are easy to give, my friend. Try stepping into my shoes and then we'll see what you have to say. Goodbye." Saying so, a broken Sunil turned around and slowly walked away.

Anil watched him leave and thought to himself, "This is most unfortunate. He really was an exceptional football player. Who could have imagined his fine chance would end this way. I wonder what will become of him after this. He is right. It is easy for me to give advice. But what on earth will he do now?"

Sunil had no clue either. For days, he shut himself in his room and refused to meet anyone. His parents grew anxious and fretted over his state every day. Finally, one morning, having exhausted all her tears, his mother lost her patience. She kept knocking on his door until he was forced to open it and face her.

"What is it, Ma? Leave me alone!" he said in exasperation.

"Enough is enough! This has gone on for too long. Two whole months have passed and you have had adequate time to feel sorry for yourself. And so have we..." she said, faltering for a moment. "It is time to get over this now. You are alive and well. Surely there are things you can find to do with this life."

"Like what?" he asked sullenly.

"I don't know, son. I wish I did, but I don't. You *have* to find something new that interests you. You can't just spend all your time sitting alone in this room."

"Let it be, Ma. Just leave me alone. We've been through this drill many times before. It's not going to have any effect on me anymore. None of you can even begin to imagine the state of mind I am in at this time. Be honest with yourself, Ma. What reason can you give me to step out of here after all that has happened? You say I should find something else that interests me. Frankly, I just don't want to now. What I actually wanted, I will never get. Whatever I had done so far, was all for nothing. I cannot think of doing anything else. All I want is to be by myself and not have anyone intrude into my privacy, be it friends or family."

It took a few moments for Sunil's mother to absorb her son's angry outburst. She could intuitively sense the agony and dejection that lay behind his claim of refusing all company. A glimpse of the disarray his room was in, made it worse. Clothes were scattered all over haphazardly, used cups and empty soda cans lay strewn all around and the sheet meant to cover the bed covered the dirty floor instead. Before she could try and say something to comfort her son, he shut the door on her and retreated to his reclusive lifestyle.

Unable to bear seeing her son in his present condition, Sunil's mother immediately went to her husband and poured her heart out, urging him to think of some kind of a solution soon, before it was too late. "It is not only his physical health I am worried about. He had just about got over his depression regarding the accident and Anil's loss, and had focused all his attention on returning to the team. What if this rejection takes him back into that dark space again? After so much encouragement, he had finally stepped out of his shell, and now this! What if he loses his fighting spirit altogether this time? How is Sunil going to battle all this? How are any of us going to do so? We have both tried our best to talk to him, to get him to talk to us. But he just refuses to listen. What are we going to do?"

For his part, Sunil remained quiet and morose. All attempts to engage him in conversation failed. One morning, however, when he stepped out of his room, a minor quarrel with his mother, over not being able to find a favourite teacup, ended up becoming the occasion for him to let out all that was bottled up inside. "I can't bear this anymore, Ma. As much as I am irked by my broken body and spirit, I am worried more about the suffering I am putting you and Papa through. I am too tired now to think straight or be brave or... do anything," he said, turning his face away to hide the tears starting to run down his cheeks.

His mother could not let this chance go. "Sunil, please... We have to take some help. You are right. If this is taking its toll on you, it is also doing so on your father and me. This is not the time to be stubborn. Please. Are you willing to get some counselling?"

Sunil shook his head fiercely to reject the idea. "No! Why do I need to go to a counsellor? I am not insane!"

"Of course you are not, Sunil. Taking help from a professional does not mean you are insane. If the three of us cannot solve a particular problem, is it not better to consult an expert in the matter? I don't see any harm in that."

After some persuasion, Sunil finally gave in. "Alright, I have my doubts if this will work, but what have I got to lose anyway. However, please find a counsellor who does not prescribe any medication or drugs."

After a long and diligent search, Sunil's mother finally decided to request a counsellor named Anushka to take up her son's case. A close friend had recommended her, confessing that she too had sought help from her during a difficult time in her marriage and it had made quite a difference. Somewhat reluctantly then, Sunil agreed to start his counselling sessions and was on his way for his first meeting with Anushka.

After a warm welcome and handshake, Sunil opened up to her tentatively with, "I hope you will help me find some answers; answers as to why this has happened, why my dreams have been shattered, and what I am supposed to do with myself now."

Anushka responded politely but firmly, "Sunil, I will do my best to help you. But before we begin, we need to come to one clear understanding. Though this might sound rather strange to you, you must not expect me to provide any simple black and white answers. In fact, I would even go further and say, I cannot do that."

Sunil was perplexed, "But providing answers is what you are supposed to do, isn't it? Isn't that the reason I am here?"

"Yes, I know you do need some answers. But all I am saying is that, finally, I will not be the one providing them. Sure, I will help you as much as I can in your search for them, but ultimately, it is you who has to decide which way you wish to go. If anything, one of the most important things my job involves is to give you more questions..." She paused for a moment, smiling at his startled expression. "Yes, questions you need to ask yourself and think about; questions that will propel you to re-examine your existing habits of thinking and change them if necessary. Does that make any sense to you?"

Sunil slowly nodded in acquiescence. Such forthrightness, such clarity and simplicity was a welcome relief for him, whose mind, muddled by the various disturbing thoughts that had been racing through it since the last several weeks, had been thirsting for such solace. He had come prepared for one of those age-old cliché filled motivational speeches, but this frankness was most unexpected.

"Ok then, the first thing I want to know from you is, how long it has been since you have met any of your friends?"

"Well, it's been a little more than two months..."

"Hmm... And why has that been the case? One can understand the need to be alone immediately after your rejection from the team, but why have you continued to isolate yourself from everyone even after that?"

"Well, I don't really think any of them can empathize with what I have gone through and all they can offer is empty platitudes such as 'Everything will be alright' etc., which I am completely fed up of hearing. So I don't feel like spending time with them anymore and don't take their calls or meet them."

"But Sunil, have you ever thought of what is it exactly that you expect them to do for you, for you to be satisfied with their behavior as friends? What would you have done if you were in their place? You cannot really expect others to stop living their own lives, indefinitely neglect their own responsibilities and devote themselves only to your problems, even if they are as serious as the ones you are facing, right? It is not their fault you have to go through this, so what is the point of distancing yourselves from them? I'm sure each of your good friends must feel extremely bad about the state you are in and would like to help you in whatever way they can. They are not counsellors and perhaps do not have the understanding or the depth to give you advice which can radically change your life and make all your pain go away, but I am sure they wish to stand by you in their own way. Do recognize that, and do not be dismissive of it. And don't you miss the fun you had laughing and chatting with them when you met? Did those little moments not lift your spirits? Come on now, I would like you to get back in touch with your friends. Do begin working towards it from today. Yes, you have to face your difficulties on your own. But meet them just for the people they are, because you are fond of them for who they are, and just for that and no other reason. Go ahead, try this out for a start."

"But what does this really have to do with solving my present crisis? Do you really think it is that important? I would much rather be by myself in my room… there are too many thoughts bothering me right now."

"It is important, Sunil. Participating in life is as important as thinking about it. If you have some questions you wish to find answers to, there is a healthy way to go about searching for them and there is an unhealthy way to do so. You say you need a reason to step out of that room, but unless you step out of this self-imposed prison, you may never find that reason again. Do not forget that we humans are extremely adept at deceiving ourselves, and, though this may sound harsh to you, I can already sense that a fair amount of slothfulness, fear and shame also play a part in your not wanting to meet other people. It is not uncommon to have a conflicting mix of motivations and emotions at the same time. A part of you will also want to step out. My suggestion to you is that the clarity you desire lies both within your room and outside of it. Focus on the small things, Sunil, they are always the foundation. Focus on your everyday life. The burden of past events will continue to haunt you for a while and the pain it has caused will not go away all at once. Continue to work on sorting yourself out, but also balance this with paying attention to your near and dear ones; people who, with their imperfections and limitations, have stood by you through thick and thin. Do not let excessive self-absorption distance you from the ones you love."

With these words ended Sunil's first brief meeting with Anushka and he took his leave, quite intrigued by the depth of the few lines his counsellor had spoken. The sessions commenced formally the next week and he had plenty to think about and work on.

Every week, Anushka would take up an issue she considered important for Sunil's development and have him examine it himself from a variety of different perspectives. Often, she would encounter stiff resistance. Sunil would stubbornly insist on the darkness and hopelessness he saw in the situation, while Anushka would remain firm and, through her insistent questioning, try to make Sunil look at it differently. "Yes, there is a dark side to the situation. Yes, it is unfortunate that it has happened. But is that all there is to it? Are there no other aspects to the situation you can focus on so that you can come out of it positively? Why must you assume that the only way to respond to the situation is negatively? Can you see anything good that came out of this? What did it teach you? What quality has this experience developed in you? Ask yourself, why has it happened? Introspect honestly, not placing unnecessary blame, either on others or on yourself, and see what role you had to play for the situation to have come about the way it did? What can you change about yourself so that this does not happen again? What was it in the situation that you could control but did not? What was it that you did not have any control over and could not have done anything about? If some of your beliefs about your own life or life in general have failed the test of experience, ask yourself if you should still continue to hold on to them or reassess them. Think carefully before arriving at your conclusions, and be as objective as you can, so that at the end of it, you are confident of your own explanation of what happened and why, and can trust it and you find your peace. What others think of you then, will be of little consequence. However, as I had mentioned earlier, be wary of self-deception and don't manipulate either the questions you ask yourself or the answers you give yourself such that your own shortcomings are minimised. We tend to paint pictures that make us look good, often at the cost of the truth."

A common hindrance in the sessions would be phases where Sunil, though overtly seeming to grapple with his problems, would somewhere begin to wallow in the doubt that self-analysis brings with it and use it as an excuse to not move forward.

On such occasions, Anushka did not mince her words and expressed strong disapproval. "Sunil, the fact that you continue to come for these sessions indicates that there is a part of you that has not given up yet and wants to live a healthier, wiser and happier life. If that requires you to confront certain negative aspects of your personality, it is up to you to take initiative and display the courage to do what is required. I am not here to encourage you to feel sorry for yourself. If that is what you want, you are free to discontinue our sessions at any time.

"Sunil, you were so determined and worked so hard to return to your game when you wanted to. Granted, it did not happen, but did you not learn anything from that? Can you not see how strong you are? Can you not use the same determination to achieve some other purpose in life?"

Thus, with Anushka to aid him through his journey of self inquiry, Sunil began to understand himself better. Regular with his sessions and following her suggestions attentively, he, slowly but surely, began to internalise the rigorous questioning and clarity of reasoning that Anushka had sought to inculcate in him. Taking her advice, he also began the simple and therapeutic task of writing a diary. The result was that he began to feel increasingly confident, enthusiastic and eager to explore the life he had earlier dismissed as worthless. He now knew that he had the tools and the support to help him face his demons, and he was more than willing to exorcize them.

Six months having passed, Sunil walked into his session one day with a broad smile on his face. "I am going to do most of the talking today, Anushka."

Anushka raised an enquiring eyebrow, wondering what this was about.

"I did not tell you about it, but I have been doing a life review of sorts in the last four weeks. The way you have helped me see events in their specificity finally made it possible for me to look at my life with some objectivity and helped me let go of all my pent up emotions. Anushka, I have come to realize that one of my main complaints against life was *why* the accident happened to me of all people, and that too at such a pivotal stage in my life. When I continued to ask myself this question, I hit upon another one. 'Why not me?' I asked myself. Am I not a human being like everybody else? And so many people have suffered tragic accidents in so many ways, so on what basis should I consider myself an exception? It was *my* dream to become a national level football player, I believed it was my destiny and I worked towards it out of my own free will, but life has its own plans as well. In fact, if one thinks about it, the only certainty that life really offers one, apart from birth and death, is this present moment. After all, who knows what the future holds? I am aware that this is an obviously extreme view, and that there is a good probability of us remaining as alive and well in the next moment as we are in the present one, yet, it seems to me that the idea is worth thinking about. It makes one acknowledge one's limitations as a human being and encourages an attitude of humility before life. This is not to suggest in any way, however, that one should simply accept all kinds of accidents or other misfortunes as 'part of life' and give in to them without a fight. Haven't some of man's greatest achievements been the result of entire lifetimes of relentless struggle and unyielding dedication? Surely, one should never stop trying to live as fulfilling a life as one can, right until the end. But an awareness of one's limitations and follies will only be of help in this process.

"If my accident has happened, well, then it has, and I must find the best way to deal with it, if not for any other reason, but primarily because I want to live life as best as I can. I want to see if I can do better, and I do not want to let my spirit die down. There is no point in taking this personally, as though life were conspiring against me. I am glad that the first thing I did was put in my best efforts to try to get back in the team. Now at least I am sure that that option is closed and I have the satisfaction of knowing that I did everything I could possibly have done on that front. I have now made up my mind to try other options life has to offer. How easily I had earlier assumed that nothing else in the world would compare to the joy that playing football gave me. Have I really experienced so much of life that I can dismiss all other possibilities that remain available for me as insignificant? It is my job and nobody else's to go out in the world and find what inspires and motivates me again, and nothing is going to come to me sitting in my room. I wish to make each moment of my life count as much as I can."

Having finished what he had to say, Sunil stopped to find a pleasantly surprised Anushka smiling at him. Delighted to hear him say all this, she responded warmly, "This is wonderful, Sunil. Your parents, friends and coach were not saying anything very different. But the answers had to come from within you. I am so happy to see that you yourself now see things from this perspective. You have worked tirelessly to honestly examine the disturbing events in your life and managed to convert them into opportunities for growth and evolution. Now tell me, have you thought of something further? How would you like to use your knowledge and experience?"

Sunil took only a moment to answer, "I have thought of something, Anushka. After completing college, I think I would eventually want to start coaching young athletes and sportsmen. I already know quite a lot about football, and would love to learn more, and also have first-hand experience of what it actually takes to perform well on the field under extreme pressure. But, as I have learnt from recent events, there is much more to living a healthy life than just a physically fit body and an aggressive mind, ever ready to compete with the world. I remember my coach, Amit, telling me when I was hurt that, along with issues of physical fitness, I must address the pain I have suffered emotionally as well. I can understand what he meant now. Not only have my dark days helped me grow mentally and physically stronger, but I also understand what it feels like to be trapped and weighed down in seemingly inescapable circumstances and can empathise with people in the same state as me. Thanks to Amit, you and my parents, I have some idea of how to get out of such a state as well. I would now like to help others the same way all of you have supported me. There is great strength waiting to be tapped in each one of us, if we can only manage to leverage it fully. I would be happy to touch someone's life in such a manner, to help them come out of a situation that has left them depressed and hopeless. I feel I must build on and share with others whatever valuable lessons have come out of all this. May I intern formally with you Anushka?"

Anushka agreed without hesitation. She felt rather fulfilled, having effectively played her part in helping someone in distress. He has travelled so far, she thought to herself. And hopefully will now be able to help guide others out of their tunnels of darkness.

I wish him all the very best. "I am very proud of you, Sunil," she said. "You may join the office from next Monday. See you then."

~

The story had ended and it was time for everyone to disperse. More at ease with opening themselves up to Areen and each other now, they had begun to interact more during their scheduled breaks and were eager to return and converse with their guide. When they regrouped, Areen, without wasting any time, said, "Alright folks. Let's get started. Who has something to say?"

Ronak was quick to respond, "Yes, Areen. This was a timely story for me. It has helped me see some kind of a pattern in whatever has been happening back home in my family. Just as Sunil was so adamant on not letting go of some of *his* dreams and beliefs about life, bitterly fighting all that conflicted with them until he finally had to learn to see things differently, I feel that all of us similarly neglect many of our problems which tend to keep growing in intensity, until try as we may, we just cannot ignore them anymore and are forced to face them; I sure would like to see what has been happening within my family in this fresh light right now. I am particularly wondering how this may help my sister, Moksha..."

Areen prompted him to go on, "Is Moksha in some form of difficulty, Ronak?"

"Yes Areen. She has been in difficulty for a long time but I suppose we just failed to recognize it. It took us some time to empathize with her... too much time perhaps. It was not until last year that we were shocked out of our indifference and had to wake up and take notice of her suffering. Just as Sunil found meaning in the challenges he encountered, I hope Moksha does too. I will definitely share his story with her. It is almost as though one's life keeps playing a song and turning up its volume until we finally hear it, right? As if our life is showing us something, taking us in some direction. When the volume is low we still manage to block it out, deliberately ignoring the song until it gets too loud and painful and we must hear it. You know, the way Anushka had Sunil relentlessly re-examine his own life, and choose a new way forward?"

"That's some analogy," remarked Drishti.

He sighed, "Anyway, let me tell you about it from the start.

"Right from childhood, Moksha was 'different'—well, at least that is how my parents put it. She is much older than me, almost by eight years, so I did not personally witness her childhood, but you know how it is at home–no matter how old the children of the family grow, the elders insist on harping on the smallest incidents of their childhood until one feels like one was there oneself when they actually happened.

When I look at all the stories about Moksha now, I realize how they clearly indicated that she had a mind of her own. Instead of the dry and mechanical learning of her school, she was always more interested in exploring the plants, trees, flowers, squirrels and insects in our backyard. She would talk to birds quite keenly and was known for bringing home every injured animal she came across. Once it was a bird with a broken wing, on another occasion it was a dog with an injured leg, and one of the more famous stories involved her rescuing a kitten who had almost died. My mother had taken Moksha to the fish market and imagine her surprise when, on coming home, she opened one of the shopping bags to have a ragged kitten jump out of it! Moksha insisted on keeping the cute little thing and, despite the ruckus our grandmother created, the cat stayed at our place until it was capable enough of wandering off on its own.

"Anyway, the point is that Moksha seemed to live in a world different from ours. She had few friends and would prefer to spend hours by herself, writing and drawing. My mother even says she often caught her referring to the trees and flowers as members of her family. Can you believe that?"

"I don't see anything wrong with it," muttered Malhar.

Ronak ignored him and continued, "You can well imagine the effect of all this on her studies. She would do miserably at school and passing the examinations got increasingly difficult every year. My parents were quite embarrassed by the regular dressing down they received from the teachers at school. They defended their daughter in vain, trying to explain to the teachers that Moksha seemed quite intelligent to them when they observed her at home. She had a good vocabulary and was an inquisitive child who asked a lot of questions. But why she fared so poorly in school was beyond them. Ultimately, my parents were not strong enough to withstand the pressure of the school authorities. They too began to scold Moksha and tried to mould her into a 'normal' child, not realizing that situations such as speaking in front of groups or being called out by the teacher in class were extremely disturbing for her. She would just be clueless as to what the 'acceptable' ways of acting were in such circumstances, and so preferred to fade into the background, hating it when drawn out forcefully. For my parents, the last straw was Moksha's deep distress over the death of a pet goldfish. She insisted on placing it in a matchbox, burying it in the garden in a small grave she had prepared, and wanted our entire family to be a part of the funeral procession. Mother and Father were convinced that she was losing her mind, growing more attached to animals than humans. Despite all her arguments and tears, Moksha was never allowed to bring in a single pet in the house again. In fact, one of my earliest memories is of my sister crying herself to sleep because she was not allowed to keep a puppy that had followed us home from the nearby playground. Her strongest support system, her connection with the animals, had now been denied to her.

"I grew up watching these constant tussles between Moksha and the rest of the world and never saw the happy, sparkling child that some relations described her to be in her earlier years. All I saw was a quiet, defeated girl who would disappear at the first sign of visitors and answer everyone in as few words as was possible. As for myself, I never really had a problem with the way she was. I found her to be kind and gentle in her own way and loved her for her sensitivity. Quite happy to be the outspoken one of the two of us and hog all the limelight, I enjoyed singing and dancing in front of visitors and thrived on their applause, while Moksha hid in her room and pretend not to hear our parents calling her out to share her poetry. Academics too, had always been a breeze for me. So, for my parents, there was a palpable sense of relief that at least one of their children was progressing 'normally.'

"As I say all this now, I realize that all of us had come to an unspoken agreement that Moksha was somehow a 'misfit' and we could not expect much of her. We had to push and prod her to continue with her education, but there was little else that could be done beyond that. We were too blind to the signs then that we began to sense only much later—that we were measuring her by certain arbitrarily established yardsticks and, by those standards, judging her to be 'strange.' There was a national creative writing competition that Moksha participated in, while in junior college, where she won a consolation prize; and the chief guest and judge there was none other than the renowned writer, Mustafa. He personally congratulated my parents for having been gifted with such a wonderful writer as my sister, but though they did not show it overtly at the time, they were not too happy to receive this compliment fearing that Moksha was heading down a dangerous road by showing an interest in the arts. They believed that such trivial pursuits were only a waste of time and had no real future in today's world, an idea which some of our family friends and relatives supported, adding fuel to the fire.

Everyone was after Moksha to turn her attention to 'less morose activities.' This sitting alone in her room writing poetry and painting pictures, no one could relate to, would get her nowhere in life. No one was able to understand the effort and skill that went behind Moksha's labour of love. The brightness that I had seen in Moksha's eyes for a few days after the competition was quickly lost when she was repeatedly subjected to such unsolicited advice. One day, she got so upset that she went to her room, neatly parcelled all her art material and placed it away at the back of the loft, never to look at it again. She stopped painting after that."

Ronak stopped to drink some water. He looked tired and guilty now. "Perhaps I should have said something. Even though I was the younger child, they did listen to me more. I suppose they thought I was the 'bright' and 'intelligent' one. I should have told them how happy she had been painting and writing, how being alone in that room was something liberating for her and need not be seen as something dysfunctional. So what if she did not like to go out or hang out at the malls like other girls her age? Is it a crime to feel happy by oneself? I could see her discomfort in large gatherings. She was most at peace in her own room, listening to music on her earphones or scribbling in her notebooks.

"But for my parents, everything poor Moksha did seemed in need of correction. When she went on to complete her graduation, they decided that she should take up a course in journalism. Though Moksha hated the idea, she initially confessed her dislike for a vocation to which her personality was just not suited only hesitantly. 'I don't want to go out there and meet strangers, Ma. I don't think I can either manage to converse with them freely or get them to open up. It is too much of an ordeal for me to speak candidly to strangers, you know that very well. How do you think I would fare in such a profession? I would just end up giving you one more reason to complain. Please, this is not for me. I would rather pursue writing fiction or poetry.'

"My mother brushed her defence aside. 'Enough of this Moksha! Step out of your shell now. You have to make a living. You have to meet people and find a husband. You do want a normal life, don't you? All this daydreaming all by yourself day in and day out has to come to a stop now.'

"Eventually then, Moksha was pushed into journalism against her will. That is when she had her first breakdown. She locked herself in her room and would not respond either to door hammering or phone calls. Finally, after many hours of pleading with her and a lot of panic, she reluctantly opened the door but was as silent and lifeless as ever. She remained that way for a couple of days. My terrified parents called in the family doctor who spoke alone with her for a while. He came out telling us that we should have paid more attention to what she was trying to say since so long, advising us all to go for family counselling. Moksha, he said, needed professional help.

"Moksha's treatment went on for a couple of months and she went along with it without many objections. I think she was cooperative mainly because journalism was no longer being discussed. However, when it seemed she was recovering well enough, my parents began to feel that, if she did not want to study further, then it was their 'responsibility' to start looking for a suitable bridegroom."

"Typical reaction," muttered Soumya.

Ronak nodded in acknowledgment. "The whole exercise was, for Moksha, just more torture. Dressing up in gaudy clothes, wearing expensive jewellery, serving tea and snacks to the family and going off to a separate room for a private conversation with the prospective groom had become a routine drill. If I felt so uncomfortable through the whole thing myself, I can only imagine how my poor sister would have felt. I watched Moksha return from these meetings looking increasingly upset. Her quiet, uninterested behavior would result in one rejection after the other. It could not have been a good feeling."

Ronak sighed. "She must have been seething inside. But over the years, she had perhaps learnt to let things remain within. One day, however, she threw such a fit that it stunned us all. She shouted and raged and insisted that we all leave her alone. She threatened that if we did not, there would be dire consequences. After that, she has gone into her shell again. She has refused counselling this time. 'It is not me who needs help. It's you people! Why can't you just let me be?' she shouted out. To be honest, I agreed with her.

"This uncharacteristically extreme tantrum from Moksha rattled my parents. They took her threats seriously and went back for counselling. To be fair to them, they really had nothing but good intentions for Moksha. In their innocence and lack of understanding, they ended up alienating her instead of connecting with her. They have now come to realize that there is nothing wrong with Moksha. She is just an introvert, that is all. It was the constant pressure put on her to change and conform that brought her to this breaking point."

Not quite understanding what Ronak meant, Arya was puzzled and asked, "Could you please explain what an introvert is in more detail, Ronak? Or perhaps Areen could step in and do so? As far as I know, it is always better to be an extrovert rather than it's opposite... "

Areen explained, "Introverts are people who prefer quiet, less stimulating surroundings, Arya. They are not shy, or lacking in capability or confidence or anything of that kind. They are just comfortable being alone or in select company. Unfortunately, in a world that has placed more stress on outgoing tendencies which always help one occupy centrestage, the introvert's behavior is often treated like something that needs to be fixed. Introverts like to establish a connection with another before making conversation or opening up. In today's fast-paced world, this, unfortunately, may be treated as strange and out of place. So, well-intentioned parents and family members try to pull such children away from the solitary activities they enjoy and insist that they become more gregarious and extroverted. But what happens when you try to hammer a round peg into a square hole? Will it not get stressed out? If you let these children be themselves, they blossom. Many great artists, writers and philosophers have been introverts."

Ronak shook his head sadly, "What is this great idea of acting 'normal' anyway? What is 'normal' exactly? The counsellor told us that about a third to half of the population are introverts. Can you imagine that? And we go around treating them as if there is something wrong with them. My family has learnt all this the hard way. Not all traumas are vivid and in your face. Not all of them are immediately recognizable. Without intending to, I think we were all responsible for so many small events that hurt and affected Moksha over the years. But we tended to look at each incident as a small thing by itself. All the pushing, encouraging, guiding, scolding, call it what you wish, it was all hurting her. And we never stepped out of our own blinkered perspectives to notice it."

Malhar spoke softly, "You should not be so hard on yourself, Ronak. You are the youngest in the family, after all."

"Yes. But I could sense it," Ronak said. "I could sense what was happening inside of her. I just did not take it seriously enough."

Sadness lingered in the air. Arya asked hesitantly, "How is Moksha now, Ronak?"

"Thankfully, she seems to be feeling better. She has taken to writing in her room and has started speaking to our parents again, although mostly in monosyllables. Some part of her sees their struggle too. She even told them that she was really grateful for the effort they were making to understand her afresh... so

I am hopeful. Perhaps we will see her genuinely smiling and happy someday soon."

Turning to Areen, Ronak then said, "I thank you for this story, Areen. Sunil's challenges were incredibly difficult too. If he could find something useful in all that happened to him, perhaps my sister will be able to do so as well. Maybe she will also agree to talk again to a counsellor and see what good she can make of all this. Now that there is more clarity about her introversion, perhaps she will be able to flow in alignment with life, rather than being forced in any way by anyone. I will take your story back Areen, and tell it to her. Wish me well. Wish her well. May it help her find peace in life."

"Indeed, I pray that she finds her peace. Here, please take this," said Areen, handing over the piece of driftwood to Ronak. "May it remind you of how our challenges can hone us into a beautiful form–even if it is one different from what we expected to see."

~

Areen asked, "It is quite late. Wouldn't you all like to call it a night"? The question met with instant murmurs of refusal.

"You forget, Areen, at our age we tend to be more awake at night rather than in the day," laughed Drishti.

"Besides, if I go by the number of mementos you have been handing out, there are only two left in your Box, Areen. One for Swapnil and one for me... Please don't keep us waiting until tomorrow," Arya added eagerly.

Areen laughed as the others supported this plea, urging Areen to carry on.

8

Meenakshi struggled in vain to control her tears as Rakesh set her bags down on the floor of the airport. Turning to say a final goodbye, she knew him well enough to notice the discomfort his bright smile was trying to hide. 'Why am I doing this?' she thought to herself anxiously. 'How can he manage Sandeep and Misty for a whole month, all by himself?'

Soon after her marriage, Meenakshi had quit her job as an interior designer with a reputed organization and ever since had devoted full attention to the family. She did not even remember the last time she had taken a vacation away from home for more than a couple of days. She began hesitantly, "I know how taxing this is going to be for you, Rakesh. Handling a mischievous six-year-old son and a feisty two-year-old canine is no easy task, especially if you have never done it before. I know how worried you must be. But you know how important this is for me. It took me months to have the courage to bring it up with you, and..."

She fell short of words to express how stifled she been feeling all this while, how earnestly she had been yearning for some time to herself. She went on trying to explain herself. "You know how much I love all of you. Sandeep is a part of me and Misty is my darling. Please do not think I am running away from you. I will be back soon. But there is so much going on inside me, I am so confused and feel so weighed down that I really have to take some time off to sort myself out."

Over the last month, Meenakshi's husband had heard her out extremely patiently. Despite her vague and hesitant ways of bringing up and discussing the topic, he tried his best to empathize with what she was going through and put Meenakshi at ease. He took leave from his job for a few days. He requested his parents to come over for a month to help with housework. When his friends, happily espousing patriarchal prejudices as absolute truths, questioned him, laughed at him or worriedly asked, "Is everything okay? This is not a good sign. Are you separating? Is she leaving you? Not done, man. This is not a good sign, the woman of the house leaving like this. You shouldn't be letting her go off on her own like this. Have you thought about what this kind of freedom can lead to?" He brushed aside their snide remarks and trusted himself instead, confidently standing up for his wife.

"This is the first time Meenakshi has asked for some time for herself. It is only fair that she gets it. What is so wrong with one's spouse wanting to go on a holiday all alone?"

Moreover, even when Meenakshi had begun to have second thoughts just before making the final booking, he was the one who had firmly told her, "Go ahead. We will manage just fine."

Meenakshi could no longer delay her departure. Wiping away the tears in her eyes, she looked for a last time at Rakesh and walked away, resolutely fighting all the doubt and fear of what lay ahead.

Once inside the aircraft, she felt claustrophobic and uneasy. Fastening her seat belt, she tried to ignore the old woman sitting next to her who smiled inquisitively. She was least interested in making small talk at the time. But it was a three hour flight and she could only pretend to be asleep for so long. Besides, there were all those tears to wipe discreetly.

Finally, the old lady asked outright, "Is everything fine? You look quite upset. Is there anything I can do to help?"

Uncharacteristically curt, Meenakshi responded, "No thanks, I am absolutely alright."

The lady continued, unfazed. "Aren't we all. I saw you crying at the airport. Not used to leaving your husband alone, are you? Don't worry. He will wait for you. He looks quite in love yet." She laughed softly.

Meenakshi looked at her in amazement. How could someone be so intrusive? She thought. Without any regard for Meenakshi's privacy, the lady seized the opportunity to go on and shared her entire life's story with her. While she was going on and on, a disinterested, Meenakshi introspected, 'Will I end up like this lady thirty years from now? So self-absorbed, so utterly frustrated and lonely that I insist on forcing the story of my life down the throat of every stranger I meet?'

She then thought ruefully, Forget thirty years from now, I have no clue as to who I am today. The only words that come to my mind when I ask herself who I am are... wife of... mother of... daughter of... sister of... daughter-in-law of... and that is about it. The list ends there and I have no further description of myself.

The old woman had dozed off by now and Meenakshi had the solitude she so desperately wanted. Though guilty thoughts of how, as a woman, she could enjoy a holiday all by herself leaving her family alone still haunted her, experiencing the first few hours in the absence of familiar surroundings and people after such a long time, was a relief in itself. The freshness and sense of freedom this change brought with it, almost as if a huge boulder had been lifted off her back, was most welcomed by Meenakshi. It was the first hint for her that she had taken the right decision and she finally let herself relax, giving herself permission to think of whatever she wanted, however she wanted. Gradually, she felt the confusion of the last few months falling away. She was now growing increasingly clearer in her mind that she had embarked on this adventure to find herself, what *her* own wants and desires really were, how *she* wanted to live rather than how others expected her to live. 'For far too long, I have been busy fulfilling what is expected of me and catering to the needs of everyone around. So much so, that I have ended up completely neglecting myself. I have fallen into the same pattern so many Indian women often succumb to, of losing my sense of self, forgetting who I am. Yes, I am a daughter, a wife, mother and daughter-in-law. But for God's sake, there are more aspects to my personality too and I have the right to explore them!'

The insight gained on the flight was to serve as Meenakshi's guideline throughout the days of her retreat. Having reached her destination, she first decided to spend the first few days in complete abandon, free from even an iota of responsibility and discipline. She would wake up at noon after a long, relaxing sleep and smile to herself, thinking, 'No alarm ringing, no lunchboxes to pack, no dog to walk and no maid to supervise. What a delicious feeling.' She would then eat a sumptuous breakfast and leisurely slip back into bed to read a book. In the evenings, she would plug in her earphones and set off on long walks on the beautiful beach nearby, the waves ever so often trying to reach for the sand under her feet. Each moment of this experience was gratefully cherished.

As a few days passed by and her mind grew, calmer, Meenakshi began her project of re-establishing her sense of self. She started by diving into her past, to try and get a sense of how she had lived life so far, hoping also to find the seeds of her present dissatisfaction somewhere along the way. For as long as she could remember, Meenakshi had subdued her own needs to the needs of those close to her. As she was growing up, being the elder daughter, most of the household duties had fallen on her shoulders. Besides, she was repeatedly given both subtle and overt reminders by her parents that ultimately she had to get married and it was more important for her to learn domestic work than anything else. In addition, her younger brother had always been somewhat of a brat. There were frequent complaints from his school about his academic performance and from the neighbours about his unnecessary fights. Again, expected to play the ever-loving, concerned elder sister, Meenakshi was assigned the task of 'setting right' her brother, who being male, was 'naturally' prone to such activity.

All these responsibilities were bound to affect Meenakshi's own life and they did. Her desire to attend a reputed design college abroad was conveniently set aside by the family. They could not afford the fees, as it was felt that the money should be saved for Venkat, who was 'after all, a boy' and, therefore, it was more important to invest in his career. Besides, how could a girl go so far away from home to a foreign country all by herself. It was not safe and more importantly, not socially appropriate. Meenakshi did plead that she be allowed to go, but eventually succumbed to her mother's emotional outburst which, as it were, was the final blow that she could not resist. "How will I manage without you, Meenakshi? You know how impossible Venkat is. I will just collapse without your help. How can you leave me and go away? Please stay." So, she stayed.

Venkat, by and large, refused to change his ways and ended up dropping out of college. With few alternatives left, his marriage was, somehow, arranged to the daughter of a man who insisted on his son-in-law joining his business since he lacked a male heir. It was only then that Meenakshi's parents started thinking about her future, until which time she had been working at Rakesh's cousin's design studio since some years. Rakesh's patience and kindness had won her heart a long time ago. Finally now, she was free to move on with her own life.

The feeling of freedom was short-lived, however. A late marriage only invited twice the usual societal pressure on the newly married couple's plans. They had a child within a year and one could not but give the precious, innocent little thing all one's attention and energy. Unable to cope with her job now, Meenakshi quit and once again, life revolved around the family and household duties.

As her life's slide show mentally played out before her, Meenakshi went through a varied number of emotions that surprised even her by their intensity. By the tenth day, she found herself alternating between extreme sadness and anger. With enough time on her hands now to concentrate and reflect on her life, she realized that all this time she had never acknowledged, not even to herself, how frustrated and trapped she had been feeling since so very long. The old, buried wounds which she had to relive, while thinking of her past, made her weep uncontrollably, and had her furiously writing angry letters to each member of her family.

I never had time for myself. I was so busy catering to your needs and protecting you… but what about me? How could you all let me do this to myself? Did it not occur to you even once that I had some dreams of my own? That I needed help too? That I had to give up on so many things for your sake? Did I not matter at all? Venkat repeatedly sucked up all the attention with his emergency situations. Mother was constantly unwell. So, because I took care of myself and everybody else, I ended up the biggest loser since everybody thought I did not need any care or warmth at all!"

Going on in this vein, she would vent bitterly in her letters, simultaneously feeling frustrated at the fact that the time to write and send them was much earlier.

During this time, Rakesh's calls were an unwanted intrusion. All she could give him, almost despite herself, were curt, monosyllabic responses. Hearing the confusion and concern deepen in his tone would often make her feel even more miserable. Her rage would turn to guilt and she would curse herself for her behavior.

One day, as she stepped out on to the beach to get away from her conflicted feelings, she saw a motor boat whirring in the distance, with a figure on waterskis right behind it. Even from so far away, this person's enthusiasm and shouts of joy were most palpable and Meenakshi could only watch with envy thinking, What fun this looks like. As the boat reached the shore and the water skier too stepped on to the beach, Meenakshi was taken aback to find that it was a woman. She looked around to see if anyone would come up to join her, but apparently she was on her own.

As the woman walked closer, she noticed the look of fascination on Meenakshi's face and waved her hand in a friendly gesture. "Hi there! Thinking of going in? The water is just fine."

Meenakshi quickly blurted out her insecurities, "No, no! I could never have the courage to do that!"

The woman paused and asked curiously, "Why? Why would you be afraid to try something that is so much fun?"

"No... I don't think it would suit me. I don't think I'll be able to do it..." she answered back apprehensively.

"But how can you say that without actually giving it a try? I am Srushti by the way," she said, putting forward her hand in an affable manner.

Meenakshi reciprocated and shook hands, replying, "I am Meenakshi," and the two began to walk together from here on.

"What you were doing there, is it not rather risky? Besides, don't your in-laws or even your husband have anything to say about this?" Meenakshi asked on the way, remembering the recent letters she had written to her family members as she spoke.

Srushti was puzzled by such questions and said, "Huh? But why should my husband have a problem with my water-skiing? And even if he does, why should I worry about that? That is his problem and he needs to sort it out, not me."

"So you are married? But I don't see your husband around."

"Of course not. I am on my own vacation. We do go our own ways once in a while. I get fed up of him and he gets fed up of me, and we laugh about it. Don't you feel you need a break from it all sometimes?"

"Umm... Actually, this is the first time I am travelling without my husband since marriage," Meenakshi answered, beginning to feel increasingly apologetic and awkward in front of this independent, outgoing woman.

Srushti noticed this and decided to change the topic. Adopting a softer tone she said, "So Meenakshi, looks like we both have time on our hands. Why don't you give me two minutes to change and then we can have a cup of coffee together?" Sensing Meenakshi's hesitation, she added, "I love to make new friends. That is part of the fun of travelling, isn't it?"

Meenakshi could not refuse. Besides, curiosity had got the better of her and she wanted to learn more about this most interesting, free-spirited woman.

Thus began the first of their many conversations. Over the next few days, Srushti shared many of her experiences as a travel website writer, impressing Meenakshi very much with her intelligence and knowledge. Though the two had met for only a short time, they became very close friends and, comfortable now that she could trust Srushti enough, Meenakshi finally shared with her friend what had brought her on this unique holiday.

"To be honest, I am not surprised, Meenakshi. You are not first educated woman I have met who has led such a sheltered, or to put it more bluntly, shackled life. The ideas that our male dominated society holds are not restricted to the illiterate or the poor or to just rural areas far away from our 'developed' cities. Their roots are ancient and far reaching and there are so many ways in which men and women alike are so conditioned to believe in the intrinsic superiority of the male that often we do not even realize it…"

Feeling a kind of mechanical compulsion to defend the values she had herself privately been criticizing, Meenakshi interrupted, "No, Srushti, it wasn't so bad… I did go to college, remember? And I even worked as an interior designer and loved my job. But after marriage of course, one's responsibilities increase. And all these Western ideas of feminism, look at the damage they cause their families. Children from broken homes suffer so much, as do latchkey children who are brought up by strangers. Also, what is wrong with giving a little extra respect to one's in-laws? They are our elders after all…"

Srushti shook her head in disagreement, "Now don't swing from one extreme to the other, Meenakshi. Demanding your rights as an individual does not mean you neglect your family or home. Try to think about what I am saying with an open mind. You say your studies could not continue because of your brother. If the issue of discrimination was not so serious, then, being the more hardworking one, your parents should have insisted that you continue with your studies. But what happened? And why was it necessary that right from your childhood you were made to believe that your destiny was to remain homebound and ultimately be packed off into marriage? And why should marriage mean that you should have absolutely no freedom to do what you want to as against what you are expected to do for others? Why should you have to wait until you almost have a breakdown, until you are so stifled that you want to run away before you even get a chance to be heard? And… and who do you think is responsible for all this, Meenakshi?"

"Umm… Society…" Meenakshi answered meekly. An annoyed Srushti's reply was, "Oh yes, that answer is right enough. But it is also you, Meenakshi. And others like you, who have meekly accepted the treatment that is doled out to you without protest. This is not your individual story alone, Meenakshi. Countless women face situations and limitations like this accepting them as part of our 'tradition' or 'culture.'"

Meenakshi was upset and argued, "But Srushti, it is not easy to be a rebel like you. It doesn't work like that…"

Srushti was very serious and did not let Meenakshi finish. Looking her straight in the eye, she said, "Really? How can you be so sure? Have you even tried? No, you haven't. Because you can only stand up for your rights when you believe in them yourself. Wake up, Meenakshi. Remind yourself that you have as much right to freedom, expression and choice as anyone else. Forget the years of training you have been given of being treated as someone inferior in some way, and forge your own identity. You owe it to yourself to try as hard as you can, the results notwithstanding."

Meenakshi grew still as Srushti's words began to sink in and stir her. After some reflection, she replied with a sigh, "Maybe you are right, Srushti. I suppose I could have at least tried a little more than I actually did. I do not know how much I would have achieved, but at least I would have been honest in my efforts to stand up for myself. I never realized how accustomed I had become to the idea of the woman not having a say in important matters. Perhaps I learnt it from my mother, whom I never saw win any arguments or even consulted in any important decisions. As for my husband, well, he has been quite supportive and caring. But to be truthful, I think he is not as orthodox as I am in my thinking, you know. He often complains of me burdening myself too much by all the responsibility I take up and gets annoyed when I do not express any preference, even if he asks me. And when I asked for this break, he was extremely encouraging. I wonder, if he has actually grown weary of my timidity and forced self-sacrifice? Perhaps I just let go too soon and left all the major decision-making up to him because it seemed easier that way."

"There you go. Now you are talking. Listen Meenakshi, if I have learnt one thing, it is that no one else is going to care for you if you do not care for yourself. No one else is going to give you respect, if you don't respect yourself."

"Hmm... you do have a point, Srushti. I have been raving and ranting against my family for the last many days, feeling taken for granted and used. But never once did I seriously object to how I was being treated, even to my husband. Never did I let them all know how I felt, how I wanted to do things differently. Beyond a point, how could I have expected them to read my mind and sort out my life for me?"

They continued talking animatedly well into the night. By the time the sun rose the next morning, Meenakshi felt stronger somehow. She turned to Srushti and asked, "What time does the water-skiing start? I would like to try it out with you today." Srushti smiled and gave her an affectionate hug, knowing this was only the first of the many changes to come in her friend's life.

Some days later, when Meenakshi returned home, she

was a different person and Rakesh could sense it quite clearly. "So, anything interesting you want to tell me about your trip, Meenakshi?" he asked.

Busy preparing the evening meal at the time, his wife remarked casually, "Oh nothing much, Rakesh… except I was most delighted with the water skiing." She paused abruptly after making that statement, deliberately waiting for his reaction which she knew would be one of great surprise.

"What?" he said. "But you never told me on the phone… It could have been dangerous! What if…"

"Calm down, Rakesh. It was perfectly safe with trained instructors and life guards around. I am not stupid. I do have a mind of my own, you know."

Rakesh was taken aback by the balanced, calm way in which she spoke and, after he recovered, there was a glint of admiration and approval in his eyes, "I see. Any more surprises for me?"

"Well, we will be having spinach tonight. I know you don't like it too much, but considering I eat your favorite chilli potatoes, ever so often, without protest, I am sure you won't mind me cooking my favourite dish once in a while?" she raised her eyebrow questioningly.

Looking at her warmly, Rakesh replied, "Sure dear. I didn't even know you like spinach. You never mentioned it earlier…"

"Well, now you know," Meenakshi smiled and said, turning towards her cooking again, "Oh and also, I have decided that I am going to start working once more. I will freelance to start with, so that we can work out between the *both of us* how much time we need to give Sandeep. I will need you to play a more active part in the parenting from now on, I cannot do it all alone." A short silence followed, while Meenakshi inwardly held her breath and waited for her husband's response, wondering if she had been a little too forthright in articulating herself.

But Rakesh was only too glad to hear his wife's confident declarations of independence. "That would be great, Meenakshi. I had offered to do so often before, but you just refused, feeling guilty that you were neglecting your responsibility if you let me handle part of it. Moreover, while you were away, I too spent a great deal of time wondering what prompted this trip. What was it that had been stressing you out so much and had made you so silent and morose, and what would happen once you were back."

A flicker of guilt flitted across Meenakshi's face, as she recalled all the angry letters that she had written to her family and torn up.

He continued, "To be frank, I too realized in this time that somewhere, it was convenient for me to let things continue the way they were and so, perhaps I am guilty as well of not pushing you all that much to stand up for yourself. Breaking old habits is hard and changes are not going to be easy. But I can assure you I will try my best; I am willing to meet you half way. As an equal. Let us work together on this. After all, one of the reasons I fell in love with you was because I could see your strength and sensitivity..."

Meenakshi could not hide how relieved she felt to hear what her dear husband had just said, and tears of happiness streamed down her cheeks.

~

Areen could feel the strain in the group as he ended the story. It was evident from the incessant murmuring among the friends both when they got up for their break and came back, that there was going to be a lot to talk about this time.

Malhar was the first one to comment, "To be honest, I did not like this story, Areen. I have still not understood what Meenakshi really had to complain about. Women are naturally meant to play the roles of daughter, wife and mother, and expecting them to perform these duties is justified. I can give you my mother's example—we live in a joint family and she works tirelessly night and day to attend to each member and take care of the smallest household duties, along with the other women of the house. She never complains about these chores or responsibilities. She can't run the business the way father does, and he can't run the household as efficiently as she does. Men and women both have their own natural strengths and it seems right that they have corresponding demarcations in their roles in society as well. Traditions evolve for a reason. What is so wrong with continuing these age old practices that have worked for so long? Do we have to change things just for the sake of changing them?"

"Alright Malhar. Thanks for an honest opinion," Areen said. "I would like to hear more from the rest of you as well. I am sure the girls would be keen to say something on this one." Ayushi raised her hand. "Yes, Ayushi, go on."

"Malhar's is a prejudiced male perspective, no doubt. Have you even asked your mother, before assuming that she is happy being locked up at home? How do you know she doesn't want to run the business?" claimed Ayushi irritatedly.

Areen quickly intervened, lest things got out of hand. "Now, now, Ayushi. Let's not make it personal. Leave Malhar's mother out of it."

Aditi rose to her defense, saying, "But she is right, Areen. Everyone just conveniently assumes that women choose to be dominated and are incapable of taking on serious responsibility or making independent choices. I think what Areen's story brought out very well was how a majority of our society is infected with the belief that women should have no say in their choices, that they should dutifully adhere to the expectations from them and when it comes to sacrifice, it is only natural that they should be the one coming out compromised. It starts with simple, daily things like buying dolls for girls and toy cars for boys and the daughter serving tea to the guests while the son sits happily on the sofa even in our so called educated families. That the best quality food go to the men of the house while the women eat only after them is also a prevalent custom. As was done in Meenakshi's case, the opportunity to get a good education is decided not by merit but by one's gender. Why, even our ancestral laws have favoured the male in the division of property. The poor woman then, after being the bastion of the household, is always at the mercy of her father, or husband, or son—her contribution is never recognized or rewarded. If women appear dependent after all this, who are we to blame?"

Drishti tried to calm things down. "But things are changing, Aditi. You make it sound so cloistered. Just as I felt Meenakshi's troubles were exaggerated in Areen's story. Look around you, here itself, there are so many females who are educated, articulate and being given their freedom..."

"Really Drishti? That is easy for you to say. Do you know how hard it is for us to get permission from our parents for even small things such as going out with friends? If you ever tried living with the number of curfews we do, you would know how it feels. My own parents rarely allow me out of the house after half past six in the evening. It is a miracle they let me come here so far away from home. The standard answer given to us is, of course, that this is done for our safety. Yes, it is true. The streets are very unsafe for us but really, why do you think that is so? Isn't it because women have been objectified, used and treated like second-rate human beings over all these years? Isn't it the mindset of the man on the street who makes us feel unsafe that needs to be changed, rather than we changing ourselves?"

Tempers were fast rising now and Swapnil was the one who spoke up next. "I actually agree with the girls. I can see what they are saying happening with my own elder sister at home. All this forward thinking and equality are mere words in our patriarchal system. I was reading a shocking article in the newspaper recently on how female infanticide is still very prevalent, even in the supposedly sophisticated urban middle-class households of a city like Delhi. Girls like my sister and Meenakshi, who are fortunate enough to get an education, we know that most of them have great societal pressure on them to get married as soon as they graduate, often at the cost of discontinuing further studies. So many of my friends have admitted that to me. Some have resigned themselves to their fate, while some are still struggling against it, trying to find a way out. But I must also say here that there are a few who are quite pleased with things as they are as well. They prefer not having to think seriously or taking responsibility for themselves."

Areen intervened, "That's true, Swapnil. There will always be issues left to personal choice. The point is, as a society, are we providing the freedom and platform for women to make their own choices? Or are they still being forced, in overt or covert ways, to meet the demands of men? Have we defined strict black and white options for them without their consent? Isn't it actually true that both men and women are actually capable of performing whatever roles or duties they choose?"

"Let me give you an example of a kind of ideal situation, Areen," said Aditi. "My mother has a young friend named Samia. She was a software engineer and enjoyed a successful career, but when she got married she wanted to take a break from work. However, the strange thing was that her friends tried her best to convince her that she must not 'succumb' to becoming a homemaker at any cost. Now to me, this is the other extreme of stereotyping—rejecting a 'feminine' role simply on the grounds that it is 'feminine' and for no other reason but that. Samia, however, was very clear that this was a part of herself that she wanted to explore and dismissed her friends' views as rather reductive.

Her husband, Rahul, fortunately was quite a sensible guy and they both understood and respected each other well. He understood that managing the house was no mean task, and that just because he went 'outside' to work did not mean his work was superior and deserved special treatment. However, the happy couple ran into some serious trouble about a year back when Rahul developed a serious heart condition. He was advised to substantially limit his travel and work. Despite the extreme hardship they had to face, it was amazing to see the care and concern these two showed for each other. They talked it over and decided to interchange their earlier roles so that Rahul is now more responsible for the home front, while Samia is the one primarily running the business. Both of them are great at what they do too.

"The point I am trying to make is that equality and mutual respect are what are essential between the sexes, and all this talk of who should say what or do what, can follow from there and can be decided as the individuals concerned see fit. Being genuinely given equal opportunity is what is most important, so that each individual can best express his own being and contribute to family and society as well as is possible for him, just as Rahul and Samia did."

"That is very well said, Aditi," said Areen with admiration.

"Let me add, Areen, that these two also take good care of their respective parents and in-laws. They have wonderful relations with them and it is not uncommon for Samia or Rahul's parents to come and live with them for a few months at a time. I say this specifically because I was outraged the other day, when my friend's parents refused to drink water at their son-in-law's house. Each time they go there, they do so with their heads bowed, bearing expensive gifts and saying things like we are from the girl's side so we must be 'humble'. I cannot believe such things still happen." She shook her head in disgust.

There was a short silence, after which Arya added with a touch of sadness, "It is a rather sorry state of affairs actually. I had never given the matter much thought before. But there really are so many ways in which we take women for granted. We really need to change things... in fact, not just in theory."

"True, Arya," said Areen. "We need not elevate women as unrealistic paragons of virtue or look down patronizingly on them as inferior species, the way we have all these years. We just need to see them for who they are—human beings like ourselves, equally capable of making the same mistakes or reaching the same heights of achievement as anybody else. Let us work towards establishing mutual respect and consideration between the sexes, such that no one is treated as less or more. If all of you are now more conscious and desirous of such a change–it is up to you to be more alert to and apply all that we have discussed in your own lives, in your own families and society; to speak up when required and to make others realize what you have realized today."

Reaching into his Box, he pulled out a miniature weighing scale and holding it aloft, offered it to Arya, "Here is your memento, Arya—to fairness and equality for all." Arya accepted it with a serious and thoughtful expression on his face. Clearly, there was much work to be done for us to live in a better world.

"It's really late, and you all must need a break now," announced Areen.

"Yes, we want a break, but please do go on after that, Areen," requested Swapnil.

Areen looked to confirm with the others, "So, we have finally made it to the last story. Are you game for it? Do you all want to continue to the last one tonight itself?"

There were decisive nods of agreement.

"Alright then, let us meet in another half an hour."

∽

Finally then, the time had come for Areen's last story and his young students were more than eager to find out what he had in store for them.

Before he began, Areen reached for his Box and pulled out a miniature hour-glass. It had a neat and simple finish to it that cleverly accentuated the bright, blue sand within. "Well, this last one is for you, Swapnil, we already know that," smiled Areen.

As he held it up for everyone to admire, Swapnil remarked "Ah! The sands of time? Though they call it the hour-glass, this one can't possibly measure more than a minute."

Watching the sand run down rapidly from the top, Areen smiled and said, "That is true, Swapnil. But a lot can happen in a minute, can it not?"

9

After two long years of hard struggle, the world will finally be mine for the taking, thought Rishi exultantly, As the fund manager of a large body of organizations, he had been skilfully building up his profits over the last several months. The number of clients in his private cartel was ever increasing, as were their expectations. From relying solely on his financial acumen, his job had been reduced to sly networking and shrewdly exploiting insider information. It was progressively more of these intricate manipulations that left him with a high adrenaline rush. The stress and pressure of these complicated transactions had been taking a toll on his health and family life and Rishi was desperate for that one large jackpot that would enable him to relax once and for all. Everything had gone as planned, so far, and today was the day he was going to strike gold in the share market.

But there are no shortcuts to lasting peace. His secretary came rushing in to announce, "It's over Rishi. The news got leaked out. It's on all the business news channels. The *Viman* stock is bound to crash in no time."

As he looked at her in shock, he exclaimed, "No, that is not possible! I will be ruined! How could the news get leaked?" But his computer screen soon started reflecting the reality of his secretary's words. Holding his head in desperation, he thought, 'Oh God! This one gamble is going to cost me my whole life. Everything. How am I going to answer my enraged clients?'

"How irresponsible of you, Rishi! I had been warning you that you were beginning to take too many risks. Didn't I tell you that I would not tolerate such gambling on your part! You haven't even left me any funds to pull out. All these years of supporting you, encouraging you... and this is what I am left with at the end of the day." His oldest client, Mistry's bitter words aptly summarised what all his clients wanted to say to him.

They did cut through Rishi's thick skin, but he did not allow it to show and bravely attempted a defense. "We all know the stock market is a gamble sir. Even I have taken a huge beating myself. You win some, you lose some, I guess."

"That is indeed unprofessional, Rishi! At least have the courtesy to admit to your error and apologize! If I wanted to gamble, I would go to the racing track. I came to you because I expected you to apply your knowledge and intelligence. Instead, you cooked up some hare-brained scheme with your friends inside that doomed *Viman* and we are the people paying for it. This is disgraceful and most dishonest. Don't expect to operate in this financial market again. Believe me, I still have enough clout to make sure you never get away with this."

The ensuing bankruptcy and investigation kept Rishi mired in legalities for months. By the end of it, he was resourceful enough to escape with a hefty fine and the suspension of his trading card. But now his wife had finally had her fill of his complicated life. Without the money and glamour, she felt there was little 'compensation' for the trouble of putting up with him. After a few shouting matches, he was too exhausted to argue anymore and gave his consent to a mutual divorce. There was nothing left any longer. No wife, no assets, no clients and no career. Angry and frustrated, he was relieved to hear from his old friend, Arvind.

Arvind had just come into town after one of his routine travels. After he finished updating him, Rishi complained venomously, "They have all deserted me, like rats from a sinking ship. No one was complaining while things were working out and more than happy to have a share in the pie. Now everyone has turned all righteous and indignant. I will show them. I don't know how yet, but I will get it all back—the reputation, the money and a better looking wife as well!"

"Relax buddy, you are better off without her and all that endless chasing after money! Come on, you know better than that. Look, you are a different sort. You were nothing like this in college. I know you went through some hard times after that, and that was what eventually made you so obsessed with financial security. But really, when is money ever enough? Man's greed only keeps growing and look what a mess it has gotten you into. Take this as a wake-up call to change your priorities my friend. Relax, let life take you where it has to."

Rishi observed the laid-back Arvind without comment. Arvind was one of his closest friends. The maverick who had always encouraged Rishi to 'do his own thing', Arvind was a prime example of what he preached. Despite effortless graduation from one of the finest engineering colleges, he chose to remain jobless. When Rishi questioned his lack of ambition, he replied, "It leaves me free to wander aimlessly, without plans or objectives. My backpack is all I need. My family has come to accept my way of living. After all, they know I love to paint. And when the collectors are willing to pay such rich sums, so what if I sell just a couple of paintings a year? My needs are less, my bank account has as much as I need. Why should I run in your rat race? How can it get any better than this?" Rishi had no convincing answer.

Rishi knew what Arvind would say next. He had heard it all, often enough. "Look, you have to trust the process of life. Stop resisting it. When you insist on doing things your way, all you get is trouble and hardship. Look at me. I have no clue where I will be tomorrow, or how I will even get there!" Arvind laughed happily as he went on, "When I took to the road two years back, I thought I would end up a beggar. But I didn't care. Life is an adventure and I wanted to live it up. And see what happened? Who knew I would be considered the most promising contemporary Indian artist? No deadlines, no schedules, no binding rules, free as a bird. You can have that for yourself anytime you want, too."

Rishi usually heard Arvind with a mixture of awe, envy and incredulous disbelief. However, today he was angry and in no mood for such advice. He had already heard enough from his clients and could take no more from Arvind.

"Oh come on, Arvind! Don't give me all that, will you? You make it sound so easy. You could afford to take the chances you did, because you waited until you had the safety net of your degree. All said and done, you would not have ended up a beggar because you could always get a job. Besides, your family is not exactly below poverty line! It's easy to say 'trust life and let it carry you' when you have all the fallback plans well in place. I have always had to make my own future and it is no different now as well. You wanted to experiment with being a beggar and you became a king. I wanted to be a king and have ended up becoming a beggar. How can I trust life after this"? he said, ranting on abusively for a while.

When he had let off some steam, he looked defensively at Arvind, waiting for a volatile reaction. But there was none; absolutely none. Arvind smiled confidently and said, "The reason it worked out like this for me is that I was not fixated on any outcome. I was completely willing to explore what life had to offer me. You, on the other hand, are always trying to prove how much better than everybody else you are in your profession and how you have cracked the system so cleverly. Do you see why you are so upset while I am not? It's not like I have not faced a few rough days on the road my friend."

Rishi grew red in the face and angrily shot back, "That's it Arvind. Who do you think you are? If my clients think I am overconfident, they should hear you... All this nonsense you spew out..."

Arvind interrupted him cooly, "Oh, by the way, I am not interested in comparisons either."

"Fine," shot back Rishi. "But I am going to prove to you that you are wrong! I can see that I need to get my act together. I admit there is room for improvement at my end. But really, two years is too short a time for one to have proven anything, alright? Nonetheless, in the same time I had built a substantial portfolio of wealthy clients and had consistently been outperforming the index. I also had a fantastic woman in my life. Within a day—all that is gone. But let's give it fifteen years and then let us see how our lives treat us. We need a far larger time-frame to decide the outcome of this argument. I, for one, plan to get things back under my control. I know what I need to do and I will do it. I am not going to be on the receiving end of things anymore."

Arvind had been listening attentively. After a thoughtful silence, he replied. "That is an interesting thought my friend. I see your point about giving things more time. Who knows how we may step out of our own narrow perspectives after a few years and things may look different. Alright then, you are on. You guide your life the way you want, and I will allow life to guide me, the way life wants. Fifteen years from today, we will revisit this conversation."

They shook hands in great seriousness, each already lost in thought about the outcome of this unique argument.

Time has a flexible nature. The challenging times seem to last forever and the good days fly by before they can be savoured completely. Though Rishi and Arvind stayed in touch initially, they never raised this topic again. It was not because either of them forgot about it, but because they did not want to reopen the discussion before the scheduled time. Life was unfolding its intricacies for both of them and gradually their exchanges petered out.

Yet, just before the pre-decided date, both of them spontaneously mailed each other to confirm the meeting at their favourite coffee shop. Arriving before time, Arvind chose a seat that would allow him to see Rishi as he walked in. He was curious to note Rishi's first impression on seeing him after all these years.

Habitually, he checked his cuff buttons to make sure they were closed. Looking down at his formal attire he inwardly grimaced at the change in himself. Perhaps Rishi would not recognize him in this professional, business-like look. He used to dress in comfortable *khadi kurtas* when they met last.

Arvind glanced at his watch and looked up to see a tall, thin, long-haired gentleman standing before him. His eyes gleamed brightly, his demeanour seemed mellow and his thick moustache and beard hid a gentle smile. The hair was tied back in a short ponytail and indicated an easy, informal persona. For a moment, Arvind was confused as to what this sage-like gentleman wanted with him. Then the friendly eyes registered and he sprang up in surprise. "Rishi!" he exclaimed disbelievingly.

"Arvind! You are looking good my friend!" They exchanged a bear hug with much back slapping before settling down.

Studying each other carefully, they both burst out into laughter. "Wow, fifteen years sure have changed the both of us! I thought you would be surprised to see me, but you completely blew away all my expectations! What's with the priestly look? Trying to live up to your name"? Arvind asked.

Rishi smiled and looked upwards reflectively, "Let me see, where should I begin? I guess it is best to start with when we last met. Oh, how angry and frustrated I was that day!" He laughed, "I would never have guessed what was to follow. I left, vowing to myself that I would prove to you how much I can control myself and consequently, my life. I assumed that correcting my errors and rebuilding my life would be a piece of cake. But with a bruised ego and a bleeding heart, it was a long and arduous journey ahead. Finding a way forward was a great struggle. I soon realized that my client's threats had been right and there would be no way for me to restart my own consultancy. So I did some extensive networking for over a year and begged and pleaded for a second chance before I got another decent opening. My past failure was a huge drawback and I had to work really hard to prove my credentials from scratch. I barely had any money and was plagued by low self esteem and sheer frustration. I hated the fact that I now had to work for someone else, instead of running my own show. I hated that others made profits off my intelligence while I was still in some ways paying for my stupidity. I now see I got really tough on myself. You know, I could not forgive myself for my downfall, for losing my credibility, my trophy wife. So I was never happy with anything I did and had to keep proving myself again and again. Initially I thought it was to others, but actually it was to myself. In the bargain, though I tried my best, I could not sustain any relationship I got into. There would always be a great lack of trust and lots of fights."

He sighed recalling his thoughts and feelings at that time. "No matter what I did, I was never good enough in my own eyes. Hence I worked long and hard, took a lot of certifications, played up to the bosses. You know, the typical, focused, ambitious guy gunning for the top! And I did make it—right through the ranks up to the CEO. With one marriage and divorce along the way, as I had promised, I was doing everything possible to control my destiny—changing jobs, upgrading skills, selecting glamorous girlfriends; secretly facing the flip side of this consumption drive and constant insecurity–poor health, even poorer relationships, remaining always stressed and unhappy.

"Well, this phase continued for almost eight years! Can you imagine how long it took me to see what was going on?"

Arvind was listening attentively and commented insightfully, "So what did it take to jolt you out of that phase?"

Rishi smiled at Arvind. "Ah, the old Arvind is still around I see! Yes, it had to be a jolt. I don't think dramatic change happens without dramatic shifts in life isn't it? Well, for all my so-called career successes and domestic failures," he grinned wryly, "The full stop came thanks to a heart attack. Quite a serious one, I was told. When it happened, I remember noticing my left hand going cold. Then there was this acute, unbearable pain in my chest. Like the world was weighing me down. And suddenly, nothing. No sensation of pain. No sensation of body! I had the most surreal experience Arvind! I felt as though I was hovering above my body. Seeing myself crumpled and passed out on the floor. My secretary ran in. She must have heard the crash of my laptop falling on the floor. I saw her try to revive my body. I saw her rush to the phone. All the while I was wondering, if I can see my body lying there, then who am I? Who is the one watching all this? Strangely, there was no panic. In fact, there was a deep sense of calm. Just a detached watching of all the happenings. As though I were watching a movie and I happened to be the starring hero. There was also a bright tunnel of light above me. I cannot describe the tantalizing pull of it. I was feeling so drawn towards it… there was an aura of such deep, comforting peace radiating from it. I looked down at my body for what I thought was a final time, and saw the paramedics rubbing defibrillator paddles together. I voicelessly called out a *No*! I did not want to leave this peace.

But suddenly the pain was back. The agony of my mind and body was in stark contrast to the triumphant relief in the face of the medic who had revived me.

"Once you know, you cannot not know. There was no question of going back to the same life and living for me. The memory of that peace remained and I was determined to rediscover it. I tried speaking to my cardiologist about it. He was honest enough to say that he had heard such accounts; of an out of body experience before. But he had no clue as to what to make of it. He told me he would tell me how to take care of my body and heal that. For my other questions, I would need to find my own source of support.

"I spent weeks ruminating over this experience on my own. The body had taken quite a beating and I was advised to rest it out. It seemed like that the momentary death had not killed me entirely, but it did kill a large part of me." He paused to see if Arvind was following the unsaid parts of the conversation. Seeing the growing understanding in Arvind's eyes, he knew that they were in tune with each other.

"This experience gave me a totally fresh perspective. I was like a starving man who had tasted a morsel at a buffet and then been turned away. I felt angry and resentful for being back! I hated the life I had created for myself and it was impossible for me to continue in the same way as before. I could make no sense of any of it. Clearly, my life was turned inside out and I had no clue as to why all this had happened. I thought of you a lot at that time. I wondered what you would have said, if you were around. Your imagined words were provocative and annoying—'Don't resist whatever is happening. What is—is.

Know that life is taking you somewhere with all of this. Try and see that. Try to go with that flow.'"

Rishi stopped and laughed aloud. "Believe me, you were on the receiving end of much abuse at that point. Though I did send prayers of thanks and requests for forgiveness also, but those came much later. Those thoughts haunted me and when you are in that position—the only thing left to do is introspect. So I finally began to consider your words seriously. What if you were right? What if there was a larger plan at play? What if I had been sent back for some reason? What if there was something I was supposed to do with this fresh lease of life? What if there was something I needed to learn yet? What on earth could that be?"

Arvind was nodding thoughtfully, silently marvelling at how much he had been a part of this whole story without even knowing it!

"That's when I began to review all that had been happening. I began to see how much I unnecessarily looked down upon myself, and asked myself if I really wanted the life that I had been chasing; blindly chasing, for so long. I realized that I did not understand myself, nor love myself. All that doggedness and hard work had been misused because I had been neglecting the most important part of my whole life–my essence. I started reading books that helped me understand more of what I had learned from you. I studied at least twenty translations of the *Tao te Ching*. I began to listen to what my body was trying to tell me. I contacted complementary therapists and found a spiritual counsellor to assist me. With great effort, and this is where the determined discipline paid off, I relentlessly worked on my mind and body to bring them back to a new, healthy state. I started yoga and meditation, through which I met many more supportive friends who helped me come back to a whole new life. With time, I found a new way of being. I had no interest in attempting to rebuild the life I had outgrown. I shifted to the outskirts of the city to have easy access to the spiritual centre I now work for. Mindfulness is now my discipline—to be attentive to what life is saying to me, and to follow it without resistance. I work and stay with people who support me in remaining constant on this journey. I have currently taken on the responsibility for the centre's logistics and outreach programs. I am happy with myself, I am peaceful and I am doing fulfilling work. I have no idea where I will be tomorrow. But most importantly, I trust life fully.

"There is no question in my mind—what could be described as the most traumatic event of my life was in fact the biggest blessing in disguise. When life has taught me that, why would I ever question it again? You were so right, Arvind. These fifteen years have given me a whole new understanding. You have been so much a part of all this. My sincere thanks and blessings go out to you every day."

They both sat in silence, pondering over all that had been shared. Arvind studied the person now in front of him. He was convinced that the peace he saw shining on Rishi's face was genuine. The humble demeanour he saw before him was the mark of a learned man, one who had weathered the storms of life to come out stronger, truer and wiser than before.

Arvind nodded his head in respectful acknowledgement of Rishi's story. As his attention came back to his own self, he smiled broadly. "Before we declare our old debate settled my friend, wait a bit. You have to hear my story first."

Rishi waited expectantly. He was curious to understand why his friend looked so different from what he remembered of him.

"For a while, my life continued comfortably along the lines of being a wanderer and an occasional artist. I even sold another painting for the same exhorbitant amount. You were right in a way. There was nothing for me to worry about, as I had no responsibilities or concerns of any kind. Life was an exciting adventure that took me to new places and new people every day. I was happily drifting along.

"But one day I arrived at a small picturesque town that simply stole my heart. I cannot explain it. I don't even think there is any rational explanation for it. But I distinctly remember that when I reached, it was late and dark. After some inquiries, I was directed to a small, clean temple for the night. There were no formal facilities, but they would give food and shelter to travellers like me.

"The place was cool and serene. The sounds of the gurgling river nearby, created a really soothing ambience. I fell asleep instantly. I was woken up by the sound of the birds just before daybreak. I cannot describe that moment of awakening, Rishi. It was incredible. I felt perfectly aware of every sound, colour and smell around me. The singing river and breeze, the gentle strength of the morning rays, the faint smell of the dying fire they had placed beside me, to keep me warm... all of it felt like it was a part of me. Or me a part of them. More than anything else, I felt home! Home! Like this was where I was meant to be. For what reason or joy, I had no clue. But I felt rooted and grounded like I had never felt in my life.

"So I stayed on for a few days, exploring the local area, meeting with the people living there, trying to understand what life was telling me. There were no clues for me. It was a typical village or small town. With the common challenges of unemployment and limited education, I could see that the land yield was no longer sufficient to support the growing numbers of the villagers and many of them had started leaving for the city in hope of a better life. I also heard the sadness and confusion in the voices of those who were visiting home; city life was no cakewalk and neither was it providing a livelihood that could really compensate for being away from their family and this heavenly place.

As I spent days interacting with the villagers and observing the local environment, I started searching for a solution to these problems. Was there any way to create employment here itself? As soon as I began to think along those lines, I was told that there were some land parcels up for sale. The location had a breathtaking view of the river, a hill to back it on one side and a clear expanse till the horizon. Such was its position and layout that one could watch both the sunrise and sunset in their spectacular glory.

"Standing in the centre of it, I had a vision of an artists' village over there. I took the vision as a sign from the universe; that this is what the universe wanted—A beautiful space where people could reconnect with nature. A place to find themselves and to express their inspirations through beautiful creative pieces of art of every kind. I felt loved and held by the land and I made a vow to honour this dream.

"Accordingly, I contacted my art dealer and shared the idea with him. He was extremely excited with the concept and began concrete plans to implement the same. I was pleased with myself and thought my role was complete. I made it clear that I did not see myself involved in the project. Yes, I would visit for stays like any other artist, but I did not want to shoulder any long term responsibilities." At this point he paused to drink some water and Rishi and he exchanged wry smiles. Rishi could see where this was going.

"So in my innocence, I believed I had played the part of the messenger and life would work out the details, right? Wrong! Things started off smoothly enough, but they stayed that way only long enough for everything to get complicated. The paperwork for the land deal was initiated and work started. But then the investors backed out. Payments for land parcels were stuck. Several of the men who had quit their city jobs and returned on the promise of local jobs, were now struggling because of the stalled project. Their families were on the brink of disastrous poverty. And somewhere in all this, without meaning to, I was involved. Emotionally, financially, physically—I was in the middle of this logistical nightmare. I had thought that the universe would take care of it all—you know—effortless ease and all that. But then I felt so naïve! I felt responsible for the mess I felt I had created and the guilt began to gnaw at me. One morning I went back to the temple that had captivated me in the first place and sat there for hours in silent contemplation, praying for help, hoping for an answer to be revealed to me. But there was only silence. After a long while, I finally told myself that this 'surrendering to the flow' was going absolutely nowhere. The gods were not showing up to outline the recovery plan for me. I may have been broke and clueless, but I certainly was not stupid. I needed to pull up my socks and work out a way to salvage this whole thing.

"I walked out of the temple for the last time. The villagers thought I was absconding when I said I would return from the city with a new plan. Their welcoming trust had been stretched and their cynical anger only fuelled my determination to architect a way forward. The next five years were an uphill struggle that you can well imagine. I had to struggle with myself to stay committed to the venture... it was not easy for me to give up my freedom and work ceaselessly towards a profitable project. Searching for and convincing investors to back this project was a lesson in humility. I learnt about compromise, deadlines and betrayals.

"But I also learnt about myself, relationships, earning and building trust, cooperation and dedication. Once the project was physically ready, for one more time, hope sprang in my heart. I had honoured life's vision. Now it would bring in the people who needed to come to this facility. Again I was in for a letdown. Imagine—you have this picture-perfect, dream retreat centre at an approachable location, being offered at an affordable price, and yet there are no takers! Our three year payback period was beginning to look more and more unrealistic! Finally, I decided life was not going to bring me anyone on its own. I would have to go out there and invite them in myself. I set out on a marketing campaign and embarked on a new learning curve.

"I learnt well. I am proud to say that I finally managed to convert this into a profitable, lively and bustling project just as I had first imagined. Not only that, we have already opened two satellite locations in the North and South of the country. I am now actively working on a proposal for the Eastern region."

Arvind stopped and looked at Rishi's thoughtful expression. "So you see Rishi? I stopped waiting for life to carry me along. I rolled up my shirt sleeves and got back in charge. That is what has worked for me! Hasn't our debate had the strangest of outcomes? Just as if we were at two ends of a bridge and eventually crossed over to end up on opposite sides." He laughed at the image and Rishi, too chuckled in agreement.

"Astonishing, really! Neither of us could have even dreamt of such an end to our argument. You, speaking of being in charge and me, speaking of surrendering," Rishi shook his head in amazement.

After a long pause, he spoke again. "It is strange, though. Some things are common to our stories."

Arvind nodded, "Yes, we both had to question our beliefs. We both had to move to a completely new perspective, a whole new way of being, in fact."

Rishi continued, "We both re-examined ourselves and discovered so much more about who we really are, our relationships with others, our respective places in the world, our roles in this life."

Arvind took over, saying, "We both found ways to live our lives in manners that make us happy and we are peaceful with our choices. We have both arrived at similar places. In a way, who is to say which route is the better one?"

Rishi observed, "But do you see? In choosing flow, I am also disciplined? I follow my practices everyday to maintain my peaceful acceptance of life." He paused for a few moments and continued to Arvind, who was nodding in anticipation of what he knew Rishi now expected of him.

"Yes, and in my discipline and controlled way of working, somehow I am also in the flow of things–the vision has panned itself out. Only, I had not anticipated the form it would take. Perhaps, in a way, my methodical approach was what life was asking me to embrace?"

They both sat silently, ruminating over their discussion. Softly Rishi remarked, "No Taoist will be surprised by this situation!" Arvind laughed in agreement.

Rishi continued more lightly, "Wow, time sure has a way of changing perspectives. Who knows what the next fifteen years will bring? Can you imagine?"

Arvind raised his hands questioningly, "Are you proposing another fifteen year review? Perhaps some things are only understood over time. After all, you have to live the experience to gain the wisdom."

They shook hands in a silent pact of understanding.

~

Areen leaned back against the railing behind him, patiently studying the contemplative faces before him, some of which had frowns of concentration on their foreheads.

Swapnil appeared to be studying the hour-glass very attentively.

Arya muttered softly, "I am not sure I have understood all of this, Areen."

No one seemed to dispute that. Swapnil finally looked away from the hour-glass and spoke up, "Yes, Areen. This is quite a difficult one. Which one of them was right? What is the right way? I will really have to think it all through..."

Areen nodded comfortably, "Relax, Swapnil. As they said in the story—some things are taught best to us only by time and experience. Stay with the story. See how it relates to your life. Remember what I had said earlier. There can be different perspectives around the same story and each one of you may get something different out of this one. Whenever you find any insights, come back and share them with us." He smiled, "Even if it takes fifteen years, that is perfectly ok."

That lightened the mood and they all laughed softly. Some of them stood up and stretched, while a few yawned.

That was when something suddenly dawned on Malhar and he blurted out, "Wait a minute, Areen!"

"Yes," Areen responded with amusement, his expression indicating that he knew what was coming.

"That description of Rishi, it matches you perfectly… Is it possible? Are you Rishi?"

There was a buzz all around as everyone now saw the parallel between the two figures and grew excited at the thought of Malhar's suggestion being true.

Studying him with renewed curiosity, a baffled Swapnil asked again, "Really? Areen? You were… Rishi? My God, can someone really change so much?"

Areen only smiled warmly, "It is possible my friends. We are all capable of being who we choose to be. Choose well."

Then, placing his hands together and looking at each one in the eye, he bowed, "Namaste! Thank you for listening attentively and sharing sincerely from your hearts. This has certainly been a mutually enriching experience. Goodnight, my friends! We will meet tomorrow for formal goodbyes."

Each one of them responded with genuine respect and affection. The wondrous strands of the raconteur's stories had woven their hearts and minds into a space of sharing and togetherness.

They knew that they would remember these starry nights and their mentor's stories for a long time to come.

For more information and articles from Sangeeta, please visit:

http://www.serenereflection.com

http://serenereflection.wordpress.com

http://sereneexpression.wordpress.com

Acknowledgements

Heartfelt gratitude to my family, friends and readers. It is their regular encouragement and feedback that gives me the impetus to put my thoughts and stories down on paper. In particular, I am deeply grateful to my father, B.P. Vaidya, who, apart from consistently encouraging my writing, has been my inspiration in many different ways.

Looking Back, Looking Beyond has undergone several transformations during its development. This final avatar is largely thanks to the significant contributions from my dedicated editor, Rishabh Maniktala, as well as from the rest of the Om Books International team. To them, I am grateful for their patient support and valuable inputs. This book would not have taken this form without them.

Others Titles by Sangeeta S. Bhagwat

It's Your Life—A Practical Handbook for Chronic Ailments
The Caregiver's Manual
Emotional Freedom Techniques
SOUL—Student Of Universal Law